Physics for the Grammar Stage

Teacher Guide

Physics for the Grammar Stage Teacher Guide

Updated Edition
Copyright @ Elemental Science, Inc.
Email: support@elementalscience.com

ISBN# 978-1-935614-64-7

Printed in the USA for worldwide distribution

For more copies write to:
Elemental Science
PO Box 79
Niceville, FL 32588
support@elementalscience.com

Copyright Policy

Physics for the Grammar Stage
Table of Contents

4

Physics for the Grammar Stage
Introduction to the Updated Edition

Since writing the first edition of *Physics for the Grammar Stage,* I have co-authored *Success in Science: A Manual for Excellence in Science Education* with Bradley Hudson. The purpose of this updated edition was to re-align this program with our research. It now reflects the components of the Classic Method of elementary science instruction suggested in the book. This method is loosely based on the ideas for classical science education that are laid out in *The Well-Trained Mind: A Guide to Classical Education at Home* by Jessie Wise and Susan Wise Bauer.

In *Success in Science*, we compare the elementary student to an empty bucket that is waiting to be filled with meaningful information. My goal in writing this curriculum was to provide you with tools to give your elementary student exposure to the topics of motion, light, heat, and other physical principles, thus building a knowledge base for future studies. For this reason, I have included weekly scientific demonstrations, reading suggestions, notebooking assignments, and additional activities.

This program is designed to be used during the elementary years, specifically 2nd through 5th grade. It includes a buffet of options that can be completed in either two days or five days each. Alternatively, if you desire, you could set aside an hour a week to be your science day in which you do all the readings, narrations, and activities planned for the week. Please feel free to act as the student's scribe as you complete the narration pages and lab reports.

Student Workbook (SW)

This teacher's guide is designed to work in conjunction with the *Physics for the Grammar Stage Student Workbook*. This workbook is sold separately, but it is critical to the success of this program. It contains all the pages you will need to complete the narrations, lab reports, and multi-week projects. The student workbook gives the students the ability to create a lasting memory of their first journey through physics.

Scientific Demonstrations

The scientific demonstrations scheduled in the guide generally use easy-to-find materials and tie into what is being studied. Each one has a corresponding lab report in the student workbook. At this age, you will be the driving force behind these demonstrations, meaning that you will be the one in control, and the student will be watching and participating when necessary. These demonstrations are designed to give them a beginners' look at the scientific method and how scientific tests work. It is not necessary to ask the students to predict the outcome of the demonstration since they have no knowledge base to determine what the answer should be. However, if the students enjoy predicting or they are able to tell you what will happen, please feel free to let them do so.

Each lab report includes four sections:
1. The "Our Tools" section is for the materials that were used during the demonstration.

2. The "Our Method" section is for a brief description of what was done during the scientific demonstration. This should be in the students' words.
3. The "Our Outcome" section is for what the students observed during the demonstration.
4. The "Our Insight" section is for what the students learned from the scientific demonstration.

Any time you see a box for a picture on the lab report, you can have the students draw what happened, or you can take a picture of the demonstration and glue it in the box. For younger students, I recommend that you do most (if not all) the writing for them on the lab reports.

Science-oriented Books

The science-oriented books section includes reading assignments from encyclopedias, discussion questions, and additional books for every lesson. Each reading assignment should be read with the students, or if they are capable, have them read the assignments on their own. After the reading assignment is completed, discuss the topic with the students using the provided discussion questions. These questions are meant to help the students begin to gather their thoughts in preparation for giving a narration.

In this edition of *Physics for the Grammar Stage,* I have also included a list of additional books for you to choose from each week. They are meant to be checked out from the library, and are not necessary to the success of this program. The list is there in case you decide that you would like to dig a little deeper into the topics. I have done my best to choose in-print, widely available books, but since every library is different, the books listed may not be available in your area. If that is the case, simply look up the topic in your local card catalog.

Notebooking

For the notebooking component, you will ask the students to narrate what they have learned from the science-oriented books. They should add their narration to their student workbook. For younger students, I recommend that you have them dictate what they have learned to you and then you write this into their student workbook. You can also have the students copy their narration into the workbook. You should expect three to four sentences from a third- or fourth- grade student.

Next, have the students color the provided picture on the narration page. All the pages and pictures you need are included in the student workbook. I suggest that you read over these pages monthly so that the students get a review of what they have been learning. I have also included optional lapbook assignments in case your students prefer to use lapbooks over notebooking.

Finally, go over the vocabulary with the students and enter it into their glossary at the rear of the student workbook. You can write this for them, have them copy the definition, or dictate the definition to the students. If you choose to have the students look up the definitions, I have included a glossary of the terms in this program in the Appendix on pp. 194-197.

Multi-week Projects and Activities

This guide includes ideas for multi-week projects and additional activities that coordinate with each lesson. The pages and pictures needed for the multi-week projects are included in the student workbook, while the directions for creating the projects are found in this guide. The additional activities include crafts and other activities that can enhance the students' learning time. There are no sheets to record these additional activities in the student workbook. However, I have included a project record sheet template on pg. 200 of the Appendix of this guide.

Memorization

The elementary student is very capable of receiving and memorizing information. With this in mind, I recommend that you capitalize on this fact by having your students memorize the included vocabulary and basic facts related to physics. A list of simple poems that you can use to help them memorize the characteristics of motion, light, heat, and more is included on the unit overview sheet for each unit. Remember that these poems are included as a resource for you to augment students' learning experience and are not required to use this program successfully.

Possible Schedules

I have written this updated edition to contain a buffet of activities that you can choose from when guiding the students through their first look at physics. This gives you, the teacher, complete freedom in what you would like to utilize to present and explore the concepts each week. However, I have also included two potential schedules for you to give an idea of how you could schedule each week. You can choose to use these as your guide or create your own. I have included two schedule templates on pp. 201-202 of the Appendix of this guide for you to use. Please note that the older spine options are primary on the schedule and younger spine options are in parenthesis.

Quizzes

We have also created a set of weekly quizzes to use with this program, which can be found at the back of the student workbook. Although these quizzes are not essential, they are helpful in assessing how much the students are retaining. You can also use the quizzes as a review of what the students have studied by giving the quiz orally or by having the students fill each quiz out with the assistance of their workbooks. The correct answers for the quizzes are included at the end of each week in this guide.

Coordinating Products

The following products by Elemental Science coordinate with this program. These eBooks are available separately through our website or with a combo package.

- *Physics for the Grammar Stage Lapbooking Templates* — We have designed templates for five lapbooks to coordinate with *Physics for the Grammar Stage*. You can use these lapbooks as a means of review or in place of the student workbook. The directions for using these templates are found in this guide under the notebooking section.

- *Physics for the Grammar Stage Coloring Pages* — We have prepared coloring pages to coordinate with almost every *Physics for the Grammar Stage*. Each page has a key fact about the topic along with a large picture to color.

Helpful Articles

Our goal as a company is to provide you with the information you need to be successful in your quest to educate your student in the sciences at home. This is the main reason we share tips and tools for homeschool science education on our blogs. As you prepare to guide your students through this program, you may find the following articles helpful:

- *Classical Science Curriculum for the Grammar Stage Student* — This article explains the goals of grammar stage science and demonstrates how classical educators can utilize the tools they have at their disposal to reach these goals.
  - http://elementalblogging.com/classical-science-curriculum-grammar/
- *Scientific Demonstrations vs. Experiments* — This article shares about these two types of scientific tests and points out how to use scientific demonstrations or experiments in your homeschool.
  - http://elementalscience.com/blogs/news/89905795-scientific-demonstrations-or-experiments
- *The Basics of Notebooking* — This article clarifies what notebooking is and describes how this method can be a beneficial addition to your homeschool.
  - http://sassafrasscience.com/what-is-notebooking/

Additional Resources

The following page contains quick links to the activities suggested in this guide along with several helpful downloads:
- https://elementalscience.com/blogs/resources/pgs

Final Thoughts

As the author and publisher of this curriculum, I encourage you to contact us with any questions or problems that you might have concerning *Physics for the Grammar Stage* at support@ elementalscience.com. We will be more than happy to answer them as soon as we are able. You may also get additional help at our yahoo group (http://groups.yahoo.com/group/elemental_science/). I hope that you enjoy *Physics for the Grammar Stage*!

Required Book List

The following books are scheduled for use in this guide. You will need to purchase them or find a suitable substitute to complete this program.

Encyclopedias

First 6 Units (Choose the age-appropriate option.)

- *Usborne Science Encyclopedia (best for 3rd through 5th grade)* **OR**
- *The Usborne Children's Encyclopedia* **AND** *The DK Children's Encyclopedia (best for 1st through 3rd grade)*
- **(Optional Additional Resource)** *Basher Science Physics: Why Matter Matters!*

Engineering Unit (Choose the age-appropriate option.)

- *Basher Science Engineering: The Riveting World of Buildings and Machines (all ages)*
- **(Optional Additional Resource)** *Usborne Science Encyclopedia*

Scientist Studies (You can also choose another option based on what your library offers.)

Thomas Edison (Week 5 of the Light Unit)
- *Who Was Thomas Alva Edison* by Margaret Frith

Issac Newton (Week 4 of the Motion Unit)
- *Who Was Isaac Newton?* by Janet B. Pascal

Scientific Demonstration Books

You will need the following book to complete the scientific demonstrations in this program.

- *Janice VanCleave's Physics for Every Kid*

Additional Books Listed by Week

The books listed below are completely optional! They are not required to complete this program. Instead, this list is merely a suggestion of the additional books that are available to enhance your studies. This list is by no means exhaustive.

Energy Unit

Energy Week 1
- *Energy (Science Readers)* by Suzanne I. Barchers
- *Energy (True Books: Physical Science)* by Matt Mullins
- *Energy Makes Things Happen (Let's-Read-and-Find-Out Science 2)* by Kimberly Brubaker Bradley and Paul Meisel

Energy Week 2
- *Sun Power: A Book about Renewable Energy (Earth Matters)* by Esther Porter

- *Wind Energy: Blown Away! (Powering Our World)* by Amy S. Hansen
- *Solar Energy: Running on Sunshine (Powering Our World)* by Amy S. Hansen
- *Energy from the Sun (Rookie Read-About Science)* by Allan Fowler
- *Biomass Power (Let's Discuss Energy Resources)* by Richard Spilsbury
- *Fossil Fuel Power (Let's Discuss Energy Resources)* by Richard Spilsbury

Energy Week 3

- *Nuclear Energy: Amazing Atoms (Powering Our World)* by Amy S. Hansen
- *Nuclear Energy (Saving the Planet Through Green Energy)* by Colin Grady
- *Nuclear Energy (Discovery Channel School Science)* by Michael Burgan and Nancy Cohen
- *Nuclear Meltdowns (True Books)* by Peter Benoit
- *Nuclear Power (Energy for Today)* by Tea Benduhn

Energy Week 4

- *Energy: Heat, Light, and Fuel (Amazing Science)* by Darlene R. Stille and Sheree Boyd
- *Temperature: Heating Up and Cooling Down (Amazing Science)* by Darlene R. Stille and Sheree Boyd
- *Temperature (Blastoff! Readers: Understanding Weather)* by Kristin Schuetz
- *What Is Temperature? (Weather Close-Up)* by Robin Johnson
- *Temperature (Blastoff! Readers Level 4: First Science)* by Kay Manolis

Energy Week 5

- *How Heat Moves (Science Readers)* by Sharon Coan
- *The Energy That Warms Us: A Look at Heat (Lightning Bolt Books)* by Jennifer Boothroyd

Light Unit

Light Week 1

- *Light Is All Around Us (Let's-Read-and-Find-Out Science 2)* by Wendy Pfeffer and Paul Meisel
- *All About Light (Rookie Read-About Science)* by Lisa Trumbauer
- *Day Light, Night Light: Where Light Comes From (Let's-Read-and-Find-Out Science 2)* by Dr. Franklyn M. Branley and Stacey Schuett

Light Week 2

- *Pantone: Colors* by Pantone and Helen Dardik
- *All the Colors of the Rainbow (Rookie Read-About Science)* by Allan Fowler
- *Color Day Relay (The Magic School Bus Chapter Book)* by Gail Herman and Hope Gangloff

Light Week 3

- *Shadows and Reflections (Light All Around Us)* by Daniel Nunn
- *Shadows and Reflections* by Tana Hoban
- *What Are Shadows and Reflections? (Light & Sound Waves Close-Up)* by Robin Johnson

Light Week 4

- *Light: Shadows, Mirrors, and Rainbows (Amazing Science)* by Natalie M. Rosinsky

Light Week 5

- *National Geographic Readers: Thomas Edison (Readers Bios)* by Barbara Kramer
- *A Wizard from the Start: The Incredible Boyhood and Amazing Inventions of Thomas Edison* by Don Brown
- *Thomas Edison: The Great Inventor (DK Readers)* by Caryn Jenner

Sound Unit

Sound Week 1

- *Sound: Loud, Soft, High, and Low (Amazing Science)* by Natalie M. Rosinsky and Matthew John
- *Sounds All Around (Let's-Read-and-Find-Out Science 1)* by Wendy Pfeffer and Anna Chernyshova
- *All About Sound (Rookie Read-About Science)* by Lisa Trumbauer

Sound Week 2

- *Sound Waves and Communication (Science Readers)* by Jenna Winterberg
- *What Are Sound Waves? (Light & Sound Waves Close-Up)* by Robin Johnson
- *Sound Waves (Energy in Action)* by Ian F. Mahaney
- *The Science of Sound Waves (Catch a Wave)* by Robin Johnson

Sound Week 3

- *How Does Sound Change? (Light and Sound Waves Close-Up)* by Robin Johnson (Author)
- *How Sound Moves (Science Readers: Content and Literacy)* by Sharon Coan
- *Waves and Information Transfer (Catch a Wave)* by Heather C Hudak

Sound Week 4

- *The Science of Music (Super-Awesome Science)* by Cecilia Pinto McCarthy
- *Science of Music: Discovering Sound (Science in Action)* by Karen Latchana Kenney
- *Musical Instruments (How Things Work)* by Ade Deane-pratt

Electricity Unit

Electricity Week 1

- *The Magic School Bus And The Electric Field Trip* by Joanna Cole and Bruce Degan
- *Switch On, Switch Off (Let's-Read-and-Find-Out Science 2)* by Melvin Berger
- *Electricity (Science Readers: Content and Literacy)* by Hugh Westrup
- *You Wouldn't Want to Live Without Electricity* by Ian Graham and Rory Walker

Electricity Week 2

- *Circuits (Science Readers: Content and Literacy)* by Theodore Buchanan
- *Making a Circuit (It's Electric!)* by Chris Oxlade
- *How Batteries Work (Connect with Electricity)* by Victoria G. Christensen
- *How Does a Battery Work? (Electrified!)* by Roman Wilson

Electricity Week 3

- *What Makes a Magnet? (Let's-Read-and-Find-Out Science 2)* by Franklyn M. Branley and True Kelley
- *Magnets: Pulling Together, Pushing Apart (Amazing Science)* by Natalie M. Rosinsky and Sheree Boyd
- *What Magnets Can Do (Rookie Read-About Science)* by Allan Fowler
- *A Look at Magnets (Science Builders)* by Barbara Alpert

Electricity Week 4

- *Encyclopedia of Electronic Components Volume 1: Resistors, Capacitors, Inductors, Switches, Encoders, Relays, Transistors* by Charles Platt

Electricity Week 5

- *Grace Hopper: Queen of Computer Code (People Who Shaped Our World)* by Laurie Wallmark and Katy Wu
- *How to Code: A Step-By-Step Guide to Computer Coding* by Max Wainewright
- *Who Says Women Can't Be Computer Programmers?: The Story of Ada Lovelace* by Tanya Lee Stone and Marjorie Priceman

Forces Unit

Forces Week 1

- *Forces Make Things Move (Let's-Read-and-Find-Out Science 2)* by Kimberly Bradley and Paul Meisel
- *Forces (Science Readers)* by Debra J. Housel
- *Push and Pull (Rookie Read-About Science)* by Patricia J. Murphy
- *Pushes and Pulls (TIME FOR KIDS® Nonfiction Readers)* by Sharon Coan

Forces Week 2

- *Balances (Science Tools)* by Adele D. Richardson
- *Make it Balance (Let's Explore Science)* by Claudette Williams
- *Balance (First Step Nonfiction Simple Tools)* by Sheila Rivera

Forces Week 3

- *Gravity Is a Mystery (Let's-Read-and-Find-Out Science 2)* by Dr. Franklyn M. Branley and Edward Miller
- *Gravity (Blastoff! Readers: First Science)* by Kay Manolis
- *Gravity (First Step Nonfiction Forces and Motion)* by Robin Nelson
- *What Is Gravity? (Rookie Read-About Science)* by Lisa Trumbauer
- *You Wouldn't Want to Live Without Gravity!* by Anne Rooney and Mark Bergin

Forces Week 4

- *Friction (True Books: Physical Science) by Matt Mullins*
- *Friction (Science Readers: Content and Literacy)* by Suzanne I. Barchers
- *What Is Friction? (Rookie Read-About Science)* by Lisa Trumbauer and David Larwa

📕 *Why Do Moving Objects Slow Down?: A Look at Friction* by Jennifer Boothroyd

Forces Week 5

📕 *What Floats? What Sinks?: A Look at Density* by Jennifer Boothroyd

📕 *Dive! Dive! Dive!: Buoyancy (Raintree Fusion: Physical Science)* by Isabel Thomas

Motion Unit

Motion Week 1

📕 *Motion (Science Readers: Content and Literacy)* by Debra Housel

📕 *And Everyone Shouted, "Pull!": A First Look at Forces and Motion* by Claire Llewellyn and Simone Abel

📕 *Motion: Push and Pull, Fast and Slow (Amazing Science)* by Darlene R. Stille and Sheree Boyd

Motion Week 2

📕 *Motion (Blastoff! Readers: First Science)* by Kay Manolis

📕 *Vroom! Speed and Acceleration (TIME FOR KIDS® Nonfiction Readers)* by Stephanie Paris

📕 *Full Speed Ahead!: How Fast Things Go* by Cruschiform

Motion Week 3

📕 There are no additional books for this week.

Motion Week 4

📕 *Isaac Newton: The Scientist Who Changed Everything (National Geographic World History Biographies)* by Philip Steele

📕 *Isaac Newton (Giants of Science)* by Kathleen Krull and Boris Kulikov

📕 *Isaac Newton and the Laws of Motion* by Andrea Gianopoulos and Charles Barnett III

Engineering Unit

Engineering Week 1

📕 *Roll, Slope, and Slide: A Book About Ramps (Amazing Science: Simple Machines)* by Michael Dahl and Denise Shea

📕 *Ramps (Simple Machines: Blastoff Readers, Level 4)* by Kay Manolis

📕 *Levers (Simple Machines: Blastoff Readers, Level 4)* by Kay Manolis

📕 *Levers in Action (Simple Machines at Work)* by Gillian Gosman

📕 *Screws (Simple Machines)* by Martha E. H. Rustad

📕 *Screws (Blastoff! Readers: Simple Machines, Level 4)* by Kay Manolis

Engineering Week 2

📕 *Wheels and Axles (Simple Machines)* by Martha E. H. Rustad

📕 *Gears Go, Wheels Roll (Science Starts)* by Mark Weakland

📕 *Pulleys and Gears (Simple Machines)* by David Glover

- *Pull, Lift, and Lower: A Book About Pulleys* by Michael Dahl and Denise Shea
- *Simple Machines: Wheels, Levers, and Pulleys* by David A. Adler and Anna Raff

Engineering Week 3
- *Simple Machines (Let's-Read-and-Find-Out Science 2)* by D. J. Ward and Mike Lowery
- *Simple Machines: Real Size Science* by Rebecca Rissman
- *Simple Machines (Rookie Read-About Science)* by Allan Fowler
- *How Machines Work: Zoo Break!* by David Macaulay

Engineering Week 4
- *Engineers Solve Problems (Engineering Close-Up)* by Reagan Sikkens Miller
- *Rosie Revere's Big Project Book for Bold Engineers* by Andrea Beaty and David Roberts

Engineering Week 5
- *Concrete Mixers (Blastoff! Readers: Mighty Machines, Level 1)* by Ray McClellan
- *Steel (Recycle, Reduce, Reuse, Rethink)* by Kate Walker
- *Plastic (Everyday Materials)* by Andrew Langley
- *Plastic (Reduce, Reuse, Recycle)* by Alexandra Fix
- *What Milly Did: The Remarkable Pioneer of Plastics Recycling* by Elise Moser and Scot Ritchie

Engineering Week 6
- *Building America - Gateway Arch* by Craig A. Doherty and Katherine M. Doherty
- *Bridges (True Bookengineering Wonders)* by Katie Marsico
- *Building Bridges (Young Engineers)* by Tammy Enz
- *Tunnels (21st Century Junior Library: Extraordinary Engineering)* by Virginia Loh-Hagan Edd
- *The Channel Tunnel (Great Building Feats)* by Sandra Donovan

Engineering Week 7
- *Cars, Trains, Ships, and Planes* by DK Publishing
- *Car Science* by Richard Hammond
- *I Wonder Why Planes Have Wings: And Other Questions About Transportation* by Christopher Maynard
- *Submarines (Rookie Read-about Science: How Things Work)* by Joanne Mattern
- *DK Readers L1: Submarines and Submersibles* by Deborah Lock

Engineering Week 8
- *Smartphones (How It Works)* by Lisa J. Amstutz
- *Satellites and the GPS (Simply Science)* by Natalie M. Rosinsky
- *National Geographic Readers: Robots* by Melissa Stewart

Supplies Needed by Week

Energy Unit

Week	Supplies needed
1	Ruler, String (2 ft.), Tape, Heavy book, 2 Rubber balls
2	Pinwheel template, Chopstick or thin dowel rock, Straight pin, Bead
3	A twistable tube-shaped balloon, Scissors, A small marble or ball, Large box or plastic storage bin
4	Rubber band
5	Aluminum foil, Small throw rug or towel
Unit Project	Plastic spoon, Marshmallow or Small, light bead, Other materials will vary based on design

Light Unit

Week	Supplies needed
1	Small nail or screw, Box with a lid, Small objects, such as a ball, pencil, or a toy car, Flashlight
2	Poster board, Scissors, Pencil, Ruler, Markers (red, orange, yellow, blue, green, and purple)
3	Cardboard, Flashlight, Scissors, Modeling clay, Ruler, Index card
4	Hand mirror, Pencil, Paper
5	*No supplies needed.*
Unit Project	Clear, flat plastic tote, such as the one used to store things under a bed, Wax paper, String of fluorescent rope lights, Container of salt, Squares of tissue paper in a variety of colors, Clear dish, Several different clear liquids (water, alcohol, or corn syrup), Hand mirror, Old glasses or other lenses

Sound Unit

Week	Supplies needed
1	Stemmed glassware, Liquid soap, Vinegar
2	Ruler, Table
3	Cup, Rubberband
4	Straw, Scissors, Ruler, Marking pen
Unit Project	*Materials will vary based on the instrument you choose to make.*

Supplies Needed by Week

Electricity Unit

Week	Supplies needed
1	Comb, Tissue Paper, Scissors, Ruler
2	Clothespin, D-battery, Foil, Flashlight bulb, Tape, Testing materials (e.g., rubber band, paper coins, paper clip, ruler)
3	Straight pin, Thread, Tissue paper, Bar magnet, Scissors
4	Old Electronic, Screwdriver, Newspaper
5	Computer, Access to the Internet
Unit Project	Snap Circuits Jr. SC-100 Electronics Discovery Kit or a comparable circuit kit

Forces Unit

Week	Supplies needed
1	Toy car, String, Tape, Several books, Cardboard sheet
2	Pin, Index card, Scissors, Straw, 2 Blocks or cups of equal height, Ruler, Pen
3	Paper, Book (same size as the paper, but thicker)
4	String, Rubber band, 2 Large books, 10 round pencils or pens, Ruler
5	Large-mouth jar, Clear plastic tubing, Balloon
Unit Project	Washer, Box, Several shock-absorbing materials (e.g., newspaper, foam, cotton balls, or packing peanuts), String, Parachute materials (e.g., paper, fabric, or plastic wrap), 1 Qt container, Raw egg

Motion Unit

Week	Supplies needed
1	Ruler, Straw, String, Scissors, Balloon, 2 Chairs, Tape
2	Table, 2 Books with the same thickness, Roll of masking tape, 2 Jar lids, Marble, Helper
3	3 Paper clips, Pencil, Notebook paper, Scissors, Ruler
4	*No supplies needed.*
Unit Project	Build-a-rocket kit

Supplies Needed by Week

Engineering Unit

Week	Supplies needed
1	4 Books, 2 Pencils
2	Empty thread spool, 2 Pencils, String, Scissors, 2 Paper cups, 20 Pennies, Pen
3	Eyedropper, Poster board, Toothpick, Scissors
4	Ruler, Pencil, 30 Pennies
5	Cornstarch, Water, Vegetable Oil, Plastic baggie, Food coloring
6	Air dry clay, Pack of pipe cleaners, Plastic cup, Pennies
7	Sheet of paper, Scissors, String, Ruler, Tape
8	Smartphone or GPS device, Geocaching app
Unit Project	K'nex Gears Kit, Paper, Masking tape, Several newspapers

Physics for the Grammar Stage

Energy Unit

Energy Unit Overview
(5 weeks)

Books Scheduled
Required Encyclopedia
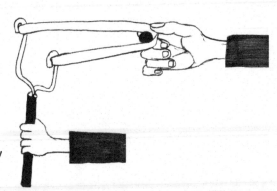
- *Usborne Science Encyclopedia*
    OR
- *Usborne Children's Encyclopedia* and *DK Children's Encyclopedia*

Optional Additional Encyclopedia
- *Basher Science Physics: Why Matter Matters!*

Scientific Demonstrations Book
- *JVC Physics for Every Kid*

Sequence for Study
- **Week 1:** Energy Basics
- **Week 2:** Energy Resources
- **Week 3:** Nuclear Energy
- **Week 4:** Heat Energy
- **Week 5:** Heat Transfer

Energy Unit Memory Work

Energy
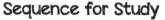
Energy is the ability to do work
It comes in different forms - each with their own quirk
Potential energy in an object is stored
Kinetic found in the motion of a skateboard
Light and sound - the energy of waves in motion
Heat is caused by temperature locomotion
Chemical, nuclear - released in reactions
Gravitational - the result of attraction
We use energy in what we do all day long
From holding a ball to hearing a bluebird's song

Law of Conservation of Energy
Energy can neither be created nor destroyed.

Supplies Needed for the Unit

Week	Supplies needed
1	Ruler, String (2 ft.), Tape, Heavy book, 2 Rubber balls
2	Pinwheel template, Chopstick or thin dowel rock, Straight pin, Bead
3	A twistable tube-shaped balloon, Scissors, A small marble or ball, Large box or plastic storage bin
4	Rubber band
5	Aluminum foil, Small throw rug or towel
Unit Project	Plastic spoon, Marshmallow or Small, light bead, Other materials will vary based on design

Unit Vocabulary

1. **Energy** – The ability to do work.
2. **Energy Chain** – A way of showing how energy changes into different forms.
3. **Wind energy** – Energy from the wind.
4. **Solar energy** – Energy from the sun.
5. **Nuclear fusion** – The joining of atomic particles to create energy.
6. **Nuclear fission** – The splitting apart of atomic particles to create energy.
7. **Heat** – A form of energy that flows from one place to another because of differences in temperature.
8. **Temperature** – A measure of how much heat an object has.
9. **Conduction** – The transfer of heat through direct contact.
10. **Convection** – The transfer of heat through the movement of a liquid and gas.
11. **Radiation** – The transfer of heat through indirect contact.

Week 1: Energy Basics Lesson Plans

Scientific Demonstration: Bonk!

Supplies Needed
- ✓ Ruler
- ✓ String (2 ft.)
- ✓ Tape
- ✓ Heavy book
- ✓ 2 Rubber balls

Purpose
This demonstration is meant to help the students determine what happens to energy.

Instructions and Explanation
The instructions and explanation for this scientific demonstration are found on pp. 144-145 of *Janice VanCleave's Physics for Every Kid*. Have the students complete the Lab Report on SW pg. 9.

Take it Further
Have the students create an energy chain for this experiment. (*Potential energy in the rubber balls is converted into kinetic energy of movement; kinetic energy of movement is converted into sound energy from the collisions and heat energy from friction, which spread into the environment.*)

Science-Oriented Books

Reading Assignments
- 📖 *Usborne Science Encyclopedia pp. 106-107 Energy*
  (**Note**—If you find that your student has a difficult time absorbing all the information from these two-page spreads, split it up into sections, read a chunk of the spread each day, and ask the appropriate discussion questions before adding a sentence or two to the narration page.)
- 📖 *Usborne Children's Encyclopedia pp. 192-193 Energy*

(Optional) Additional topics to explore this week: *Basher Physics pg. 30 Energy, pg. 32 Potential Energy, pg. 34 Kinetic Energy*

Discussion Questions
After reading the selected pages, ask the following questions for your discussion time.

Energy
- **?** Name several forms of energy.
- **?** What is chemical energy?
- **?** What is potential energy?
- **?** What is kinetic energy?
- **?** What is the Law of Conservation of Energy?
- **?** What is an energy chain?

(Optional) Additional Books

- 📖 *Energy (Science Readers)* by Suzanne I. Barchers
- 📖 *Energy (True Books: Physical Science)* by Matt Mullins
- 📖 *Energy Makes Things Happen (Let's-Read-and-Find-Out Science 2)* by Kimberly Brubaker Bradley and Paul Meisel

Notebooking

Writing Assignments

- ☐ **Narration Page** – Have the students dictate, copy, or write three to five sentences about energy on SW pg. 8. For example, this week the students could dictate, copy, or write the following:

  Energy can take different forms, such as heat, light, and sound.
  Potential energy is energy that is stored in a thing. Kinetic energy is energy of movement.
  An energy chain is a way of showing how energy changes.

  Then, have the students copy the Law of Conservation of Energy at the bottom of their narration pages.

  Law of Conservation of Energy—Energy can neither be created nor destroyed.

- ☐ **(Optional) Lapbook** – Have the students begin the Energy lapbook by cutting out and coloring the cover on pg. 6. Then, have the students glue the sheet onto the front.

- ☐ **(Optional) Lapbook** – Have the students complete the Energy Tab-book on pg. 7 of *Physics for the Grammar Stage Lapbooking Templates*. Have them cut out the pages for the tab-book and color the pictures. Then, have the students add a sentence about potential energy on the potential page and a sentence about kinetic energy on the kinetic page. Assemble the tab-book and staple it together on the dashed lines. Finally, have the students glue the mini-book into the lapbook.

- ☐ **(Optional) Lapbook** – Have the students complete the Law of Conservation of Energy Sheet on pg. 13 of *Physics for the Grammar Stage Lapbooking Templates*. Have them cut out the sheet and copy the Law of Conservation of Energy in the space provided. Then, have the students glue the sheet into the lapbook.

Vocabulary

The following definitions are a guide. The students' definitions do not need to match word for word.

- ♻ **Energy** – The ability to do work. (SW pg. 107)
- ♻ **Energy Chain** – A way of showing how energy changes into different forms. (SW pg. 107)

Multi-week Projects and Activities

Unit Project

- ✂ **Catapult** – Over this unit, the students will design and build a catapult, which will help them to learn more about potential and kinetic energy. Each week, they will add a bit of what they have learned in their catapult diary on SW pg. 6. For this week, the students will test out a simple spoon catapult. To do this, you will need a plastic spoon and a small, light object, such as a marshmallow or a bead. Begin by sharing with the students that every catapult needs three key components - an arm to hurl the material, an elastic component to store energy, and a base to hold the catapult in place. Have the students hold the spoon handle (the arm and the elastic component) in one hand (the base) so that it is parallel to the ground and the cup of the spoon is closest to them. Place the object in the cup of the spoon and have the students gently pull it gently back with two of their fingers to create a bit of potential energy. Have them let go and watch what happens to the object. (*The students should see that the object takes flight as the potential energy is transferred into kinetic energy of motion.*) You can have them repeat this over and over, varying the angle of the spoon and the amount of force used to pull back on the spoon cup. After the students are done with their testing, have them write down what they have learned on SW pg. 6.

Projects for this Week

✂ **Coloring Pages –** Have the students color the following pages from *Physics for the Grammar Stage Coloring Pages*: Potential Energy pg. 5, Kinetic Energy pg. 6.

✂ **Energy Race –** Have the students compete to see who can transfer the most energy to their rubber band. You will need several people, a rubber band for each person, and a measuring tape. Draw a line at one end of a room or outside. Give each player a rubber band and have them stand on the line. Call out "potential," at which point the players will stretch their rubber bands. Then, call out "kinetic," at which point the players will let go. Measure the distance each rubber band has traveled. The player whose rubber band has traveled the farthest wins the race! (*You can also have several trials and add up the distances to see who is the energy winner.*)

✂ **Energy Boat –** Have the students do the "See for yourself" activity on pg. 107 of the *Usborne Science Encyclopedia*. You will need a matchbox, a cardboard, two used matches, and a rubber band for this activity.

✂ **Energy Chain –** Have the students create an energy chain poster. You can have them use the one found on pg. 107 of the *Usborne Science Encyclopedia* for inspiration.

Memorization

🗣 This week, begin working on memorizing the *Energy* poem. (SW pg. 120)

Quiz

Weekly Quiz

✏ "Energy Unit Week 1 Quiz" on SW pg. Q-5.

Quiz Answers

1. Potential energy - energy that is stored, Kinetic energy - energy of motion
2. Energy, created, destroyed
3. True   4. Answers will vary

Possible Schedules for Week 1

Two Days a Week Schedule	
Day 1	**Day 2**
❑ Read the first page from the Energy spread ❑ Add information about energy to the students' Narration Page ❑ Do the Scientific Demonstration: Bonk! ❑ Work on memorizing the *Energy* poem ❑ Define energy and energy chain	❑ Read the second page from the Energy spread ❑ Add information about energy to the students' Narration Page and copy the Law of Conservation of Energy ❑ Work on the Catapult Project ❑ Give Energy Week 1 quiz

Five Days a Week Schedule				
Day 1	**Day 2**	**Day 3**	**Day 4**	**Day 5**
❑ Do the Scientific Demonstration: Bonk! ❑ Define energy ❑ Choose one or more of the additional books to read from this week	❑ Read the first page from the Energy spread ❑ Add information about energy to the students' Narration Page ❑ Complete the Energy Race Project	❑ Read the second page from the Energy spread ❑ Add information about energy to the students' Narration Page ❑ Complete the Energy Boat Project	❑ Copy the Law of Conservation of Energy ❑ Complete the Energy Chain Project ❑ Define energy chain	❑ Give Energy Week 1 quiz ❑ Work on the Catapult Project
All Week Long ❑ Work on memorizing the *Energy* poem				

Week 2: Energy Resources Lesson Plans

Scientific Demonstration: Wind Energy

Supplies Needed
- ✓ Pinwheel template or piece of paper
- ✓ Chopstick or thin dowel rock
- ✓ Straight pin, Bead

Purpose
This demonstration is meant to help the students see wind energy in action.

Instructions
1. Begin by making a pinwheel. Cut out the pinwheel template found on pg. 189 of the Appendix. (Cut on the dashed lines, not the solid ones.) Then, bring every other corner to the center and pin them in place with a straight pin. Roll the pin around a bit to enlarge the hole so that the pinwheel can spin freely. Next, add a bead to the pin on the opposite side of the pin head and push the tip of the pin into the top of the chopstick to create a pinwheel.
2. Now, have the students face the blades of the pinwheel towards them and blow on the pinwheel and observe what happens. Does the pinwheel spin? Which way does it spin?
3. Next, have the students face the front of the pinwheel towards them and blow on the pinwheel and observe what happens. Does the pinwheel spin? Which way does it spin?
4. Finally, have the students face the front of the pinwheel slightly away from them, so that they will blow halfway between the front and the blades. Have them blow on the pinwheel and observe what happens. Does the pinwheel spin? Which way does it spin?
5. Have the students write what they learn on the Lab Report on SW pg. 11.

Results and Explanation
The students should see that when they blew directly on the blades of the pinwheel from the side, it turned in a clockwise motion following their breath. Next, the students should see that the when they blew direction on the front of the pinwheel, it did not turn. Finally, the students should see that when they blew part way between the front and the blades, the pinwheel turned a bit, but the action was jerky and not a efficient as the first time. A pinwheel is a very simple look at how we can harness wind energy. In general, wind blows and the blades capture the wind, causing the wheel to turn. A windmill or wind turbine work the same way as the pinwheel, except these devices harness the wind energy to do work.

Science-Oriented Books

Reading Assignments
- 📖 *Usborne Science Encyclopedia pp. 108-109 Energy Resources*
- 📖 *DK Children's Encyclopedia pp. 88-89 Energy, pg. 110 Fossil Fuels (You can also watch the following video to learn more about wind energy.)*
  - 🖱 https://www.youtube.com/watch?v=SQpbTTGe_gk

(Optional) Additional topics to explore this week: *Basher Physics pg. 120 (Generator)*

Discussion Questions

After reading the selected pages, ask the following questions for your discussion time.

Energy Resources

? What is a non-renewable energy source?

? What is a renewable energy source?

? Name several types of renewable energy sources?

? What does a machine do?

(Optional) Additional Books

📖 *Sun Power: A Book about Renewable Energy (Earth Matters)* by Esther Porter

📖 *Wind Energy: Blown Away! (Powering Our World)* by Amy S. Hansen

📖 *Solar Energy: Running on Sunshine (Powering Our World)* by Amy S. Hansen

📖 *Energy from the Sun (Rookie Read-About Science)* by Allan Fowler

📖 *Biomass Power (Let's Discuss Energy Resources)* by Richard Spilsbury

📖 *Fossil Fuel Power (Let's Discuss Energy Resources)* by Richard Spilsbury

Notebooking

Writing Assignments

☐ **Narration Page –** Have the students dictate, copy, or write three to five sentences on energy resources on SW pg. 10.

☐ **(Optional) Lapbook –** Have the students complete the Energy Resources Wheel-book on pg. 8 of *Physics for the Grammar Stage Lapbooking Templates*. Have them cut out the wheels. On one half of the wheel, have the students add the definition of renewable resources along with several examples of renewable energy. On the other half of the wheel, have the students add the definition of nonrenewable resources along with several examples of nonrenewable energy. Then, use a brad to attach the two pages together so that the cover spins to reveal one half at a time. Finally, have them glue the mini-book into the lapbook.

Vocabulary

The following definitions are a guide. The students' definitions do not need to match word for word.

💡 **Solar energy –** Energy from the sun. (SW pg. 116)

💡 **Wind energy –** Energy from the wind. (SW pg. 118)

Multi-week Projects and Activities

Unit Project

✂ **Catapult –** This week, have the students plan out their catapult design based on what they learned from the previous week's simple catapult. As they plan out their design, make sure that the catapult has the following three components—an arm to hurl the material, an elastic component to store energy, and base to hold the catapult in place. Here are a few ideas:

- 🎋 Popsicle Stick Catapult (easy): https://littlebinsforlittlehands.com/popsicle-stick-catapult-kids-stem-activity/
- 🎋 Dowel Rod Catapult (medium): https://frugalfun4boys.com/2013/06/06/how-to-build-a-catapult-out-of-dowel-rods-and-rubber-bands/
- 🎋 PVC Catapult (medium): https://www.youtube.com/watch?v=beQsWlc0UDc
- 🎋 Wood Catapult (hard): https://www.youtube.com/watch?v=Y0e2VzLW5fE

After they decide on a design, have them sketch it on SW pg. 6.

Projects for this Week

✂ **Coloring Pages –** Have the students color the following pages from *Physics for the Grammar Stage Coloring Pages*: Energy Resources pg. 7, Wind Energy pg. 8.

✂ **Solar Oven –** Have the students build their own solar oven out of an old pizza box. You will need scissors, plastic wrap, aluminum foil, tape, an old pizza box, black construction paper, glass or metal pie plate, and a few marshmallows or a piece of buttered toast. Use the scissors to make a flap out of the top of the pizza box by cutting three sides, leaving about an inch away from the sides. Then, fold the flap back and cover the flap with aluminum foil. Next, cover the open hole in the top with plastic wrap. After that, line the bottom of the box with black construction paper. Now, place your marshmallows or piece of buttered toast on the pie plate, set the plate inside the oven, and take the oven outside. Finally, position the box and flap so that the sun's rays are directed towards the plastic-wrap covered opening. Check the oven every 10 to 15 minutes to see when your food is done. Use a hot mitt to remove the food and enjoy your solar-powered meal!

✂ **Renewable Heat –** Have the students do the "See for yourself" activity on pg. 109 of the *Usborne Science Encyclopedia*. You will need a hose and a cork for this activity.

✂ **Wind Turbine –** Have the students make their own wind turbine from home! You will need PVC pipe, a propeller blade, a DC motor, electrical tape, and wire. This is a bit of an ambitious project, but you can see how to build your own here:
- 🖱 https://www.youtube.com/watch?v=YY1oCNhD8_0

Memorization

🗣 This week, continue working on memorizing the *Energy* poem. (SW pg. 120)

Quiz

Weekly Quiz
⸙ "Energy Unit Week 2 Quiz" on SW pg. Q-6.

Quiz Answers
1. A renewable source of energy can generate power without being used up. (*Students can also include examples, such as the Sun, wind, or water, for their answer.*)
2. A nonrenewable source of energy can be use only once to generate power. (*Students can also include examples, such as coal, oil, or gas, for their answer.*)
3. False   4. Answers will vary

Possible Schedules for Week 2

Two Days a Week Schedule	
Day 1	**Day 2**
❑ Read the first page from the Energy Resources spread (Energy) ❑ Add information about energy resources to the students' Narration Page ❑ Do the Scientific Demonstration: Wind Energy ❑ Work on memorizing the *Energy* poem ❑ Define wind energy and solar energy	❑ Read the second page from the Energy Resources spread (Fossil Fuels) ❑ Add information about energy resources to the students' Narration Page ❑ Work on the Catapult Project ❑ Give Energy Week 2 quiz

Five Days a Week Schedule				
Day 1	**Day 2**	**Day 3**	**Day 4**	**Day 5**
❑ Do the Scientific Demonstration: Wind Energy ❑ Define wind energy ❑ Choose one or more of the additional books to read from this week	❑ Read the first page from the Energy Resources spread (Energy) ❑ Add information about energy resources to the students' Narration Page ❑ Complete the Solar Oven Project	❑ Read the second page from the Energy Resources spread (Fossil Fuels) ❑ Add information about energy resources to the students' Narration Page ❑ Complete the Renewable Heat Project	❑ Complete the Wind Turbine Project ❑ Define solar energy	❑ Give Energy Week 2 quiz ❑ Work on the Catapult Project
All Week Long				
❑ Work on memorizing the *Energy* poem				

Week 3: Nuclear Energy Lesson Plans

Scientific Demonstration: Balloon Fission

Supplies Needed
- ✓ A twistable tube-shaped balloon
- ✓ Scissors
- ✓ A small marble or ball
- ✓ Large box or plastic storage bin

Purpose
This demonstration is meant to help the students see how nuclear fission releases an energetic particle.

Instructions
1. Start by blowing up the tube-shaped balloon.
2. Then, twist about a quarter of the balloon so that you have two sections, one large and one small.
3. Set the balloon inside the large box and hold the twist in two places. Have the student cut in the middle of the twist to separate the two sections. (*You will now be holding one large section balloon and one small section of the balloon.*)
4. Have the student throw a small marble or ball at one of the sections and when it hits, release both sections of the balloon to fly off inside the box and observe what happens.
5. Have the students write what they learn on the Lab Report on SW pg. 13.

Results and Explanation
The students should see that when the sections were released, the balloons quickly took off bouncing into the box and possibly hitting each other. This is similar to what happens in a nuclear fission reaction, where the nucleus is bombarded with neutrons, causing the atom to split and release more neutrons and large amounts of energy.

Science-Oriented Books

Reading Assignments
- 📖 *Usborne Science Encyclopedia pp. 116-117 Nuclear Power*
- 📖 *No pages scheduled for younger students. Instead, have the students watch the following video to learn more about nuclear power:*
  - 🖱 https://www.youtube.com/watch?v=FNNKhE1FNNM

(Optional) Additional topics to explore this week: *Basher Physics pg. 98 Radioactivity*

Discussion Questions
After reading the selected pages, ask the following questions for your discussion time.

Nuclear Energy
- **?** What is nuclear fusion?
- **?** What is nuclear fission?

? What happens in a nuclear reactor?

? How does water help to generate nuclear power?

(Optional) Additional Books

- 📖 *Nuclear Energy: Amazing Atoms (Powering Our World)* by Amy S. Hansen
- 📖 *Nuclear Energy (Saving the Planet Through Green Energy)* by Colin Grady
- 📖 *Nuclear Energy (Discovery Channel School Science)* by Michael Burgan and Nancy Cohen
- 📖 *Nuclear Meltdowns (True Books)* by Peter Benoit
- 📖 *Nuclear Power (Energy for Today)* by Tea Benduhn

Notebooking

Writing Assignments

- ☐ **Narration Page –** Have the students dictate, copy, or write three to five sentences on energy resources on SW pg. 12.
- ☐ **(Optional) Lapbook –** Have the students complete the Nuclear Energy Tab-book on pg. 9 of *Physics for the Grammar Stage Lapbooking Templates*. Have them cut out the pages for the tab-book and color the pictures. Then, have the students add a sentence about nuclear fission on the fission page and a sentence about nuclear fusion on the fusion page. Assemble the tab-book and staple it together on the dashed lines. Finally, have the students glue the mini-book into the lapbook.

Vocabulary

The following definitions are a guide. The students' definitions do not need to match word for word.

- ✏ **Nuclear fusion –** The joining of atomic particles to create energy. (SW pg. 113)
- ✏ **Nuclear fission –** The splitting apart of atomic particles to create energy. (SW pg. 112)

Multi-week Projects and Activities

Unit Project

- ✂ **Catapult –** This week, have the students work on building the catapult they designed the previous week. After they finish, have them take a picture of their catapult and add it to SW pg. 7.

Projects for this Week

- ✂ **Coloring Pages –** Have the students color the following pages from *Physics for the Grammar Stage Coloring Pages*: Nuclear Fission pg. 9.
- ✂ **Radioactive Half-life –** Have the students learn about the half-life of a radioactive element. You will need bite-sized food, such as M&M's, raisins, or cereal puffs, plus a timer. Begin by giving each student 32 pieces of the bite-sized food. After 2 minutes, have them eat 16 pieces. After 2 more minutes, have them eat 8 pieces. After 2 more minutes, have them eat 4 pieces. After 2 more minutes, have them eat 2 pieces. After 2 more minutes, have them eat 1 piece. After 2 more minutes, have them break the 1 piece

in half and eat one of the halves. After 2 more minutes, have the students eat any of the remaining crumbs. (*This activity is meant to give a students a mental picture of how a half-life works. The elements used in creating nuclear energy are radioactive, which means that they are unstable and they decay with a half life. The half-life period depends upon the element and how radioactive it is. Two of the most common elements used in generating nuclear power are Uranium, which has a half-life or around 4.5 million years, and Plutonium, which has a half-life of around 24,000 years.*)

✂ **Nuclear Neighborhood –** Have the students play with the EPA's Radtown USA website

🖰 https://www3.epa.gov/radtown/

✂ **Nuclear Fusion –** Have the students learn see how nuclear fusion works. You will need at least two marshmallows. Have the students take two marshmallows in their hands and press them together really hard until the marshmallows stick together, forming a larger marshmallow ball. (*Nuclear fusion works in much the same way – two small nuclei are joined together to form a larger one. This process takes place at extremely high temperatures, but it releases huge amounts of energy. The stars in our solar system, including our sun, use nuclear fusion to produce light.*)

Memorization

🗣 This week, continue working on memorizing the *Energy* poem. (SW pg. 120)

Quiz

Weekly Quiz

🖊 "Energy Unit Week 3 Quiz" on SW pg. Q-7.

Quiz Answers

1. Nuclear fission - splitting apart atomic particles to create energy, Nuclear fusion - joining atomic particles to create energy
2. False
3. True
4. Answers will vary

Possible Schedules for Week 3

Two Days a Week Schedule	
Day 1	**Day 2**
❑ Read the first page from the Nuclear Power spread (Watch the first half of the video) ❑ Add information about nuclear energy to the students' Narration Page ❑ Do the Scientific Demonstration: Balloon Fission ❑ Work on memorizing the *Energy* poem ❑ Define nuclear fission and nuclear fusion	❑ Read the second page from the Nuclear Power spread (Watch the second half of the video) ❑ Add information about nuclear energy to the students' Narration Page ❑ Work on the Catapult Project ❑ Give Energy Week 3 quiz

Five Days a Week Schedule				
Day 1	**Day 2**	**Day 3**	**Day 4**	**Day 5**
❑ Do the Scientific Demonstration: Balloon Fission ❑ Define nuclear fission ❑ Choose one or more of the additional books to read from this week	❑ Read the first page from the Nuclear Power spread (Watch the first half of the video) ❑ Add information about nuclear energy to the students' Narration Page ❑ Complete the Radioactive Half-life Project	❑ Read the second page from the Nuclear Power spread (Watch the second half of the video) ❑ Add information about nuclear energy to the students' Narration Page ❑ Complete the Nuclear Neighborhood Project	❑ Complete the Nuclear Fusion Project ❑ Define nuclear fusion	❑ Give Energy Week 3 quiz ❑ Work on the Catapult Project

All Week Long

❑ Work on memorizing the *Energy* poem

Week 4: Heat Energy Lesson Plans

Scientific Demonstration: Hot Band

Supplies Needed
✓ Rubber band

Purpose
This demonstration is meant to help the students see and feel energy changes.

Instructions and Explanation
The instructions and explanation for this scientific demonstration are found on pp. 204-205 of *Janice VanCleave's Physics for Every Kid*. Have the students complete the Lab Report on SW pg. 15.

Take it Further
Have the students do another heat-related demonstration - "Bouncer" on pp. 210-211 of *Janice VanCleave's Physics for Every Kid*.

Science-Oriented Books

Reading Assignments
- *Usborne Science Encyclopedia pp. 110-111 Heat*
- *Usborne Children's Encyclopedia pp. 196-197 Hot and cold, DK Children's Encyclopedia pg. 252 Temperature*

(Optional) Additional topics to explore this week: *No additional topics scheduled.*

Discussion Questions
After reading the selected pages, ask the following questions for your discussion time.

Heat
- **?** What is heat?
- **?** What is temperature?
- **?** What usually happens when a substance is heated?
- **?** What is thermal capacity?
- **?** What are the two temperature scales we use?

(Optional) Additional Books
- *Energy: Heat, Light, and Fuel (Amazing Science)* by Darlene R. Stille and Sheree Boyd
- *Temperature: Heating Up and Cooling Down (Amazing Science)* by Darlene R. Stille and Sheree Boyd
- *Temperature (Blastoff! Readers: Understanding Weather)* by Kristin Schuetz
- *What Is Temperature? (Weather Close-Up)* by Robin Johnson
- *Temperature (Blastoff! Readers Level 4: First Science)* by Kay Manolis

Notebooking

Writing Assignments

- ☐ **Narration Page –** Have the students dictate, copy, or write three to five sentences on heat and temperature on SW pg. 14.
- ☐ **(Optional) Lapbook –** Have the students complete the Heat vs. Temperature Shutterfold book on pg. 10 of *Physics for the Grammar Stage Lapbooking Templates*. Have them cut out and fold the template. Have the students color the pictures on the cover. Then, have the students write the definition of heat under the heat flap and the definition of temperature under the temperature flap. Finally, have them glue the mini-book into the lapbook.

Vocabulary

The following definitions are a guide. The students' definitions do not need to match word for word.

- ✎ **Heat –** A form of energy that flows from one place to another because of differences in temperature. (SW pg. 109)
- ✎ **Temperature –** A measure of how much heat an object has. (SW pg. 117)

Multi-week Projects and Activities

Unit Project

- ✂ **Catapult –** This week, have the students test the catapult and write down what happened on SW pg. 7.

Projects for this Week

- ✂ **Coloring Pages –** Have the students color the following pages from *Physics for the Grammar Stage Coloring Pages*: Heat pg 10, Temperature pg. 11.
- ✂ **Hot or Cold –** Have the students see if they can tell the difference between hot and cold! You will need three bowls, hot-to-the-touch (but not burning) water, cold water, and room temperature water. Fill the first bowl with the hot-to-the-touch (but not burning) water. Fill the second bowl with the room temperature water. Fill the third bowl with the cold water. Set the three bowls in order in a row on a table. Have the students place their left hand in the hot-to-the-touch (but not burning) water and their right hand in the cold water. Have them keep their hands there for two minutes. When the time is up, have them place both hands into the middle bowl and tell you what temperature the middle bowl is at. (*The students should see that their left hand feels like the water is ice-cold, while their right hand feels like the water is warm or hot. This is because the hand than was in the hot water loses heat when placed in the room temperature water, making the water feel cool, while the hand that was in the cold water gains heat when placed in the room temperature water, making the water feel warm.*)
- ✂ **Heat Vibrations –** Have the students do the "See for yourself" activity on pg. 110 of

the *Usborne Science Encyclopedia*. You will need a jar and dried beans for this activity.

✂ **Homemade Thermometer –** Have the students make a thermometer. You will need a small plastic bottle, a clear straw, air-dry clay, food coloring, 2 bowls, water, and a permanent marker. Fill one of the bowls halfway with hot water. Fill the second bowl halfway with ice-cold water. Then, have the students add a few drops of food coloring to the small plastic bottle and fill it to the top with lukewarm water. Insert the straw into the bottle and use the air-dry clay to fix it so that the straw is hanging about halfway into the bottle, forming a tight seal on the top. Have the students use the permanent marker to mark the water level in the straw. Next, place the bottle into the bowl with the hot water and observe what happens. (*The students should see that the water level in the straw rises.*) After two minutes, have the students place the bottle into the bowl with the ice-cold water and observe what happens. (*The students should see that the water level in the straw drop.*)

Memorization

🗣 This week, continue working on memorizing the *Energy* poem. (SW pg. 120)

Quiz

Weekly Quiz
- "Energy Unit Week 4 Quiz" on SW pg. Q-8.

Quiz Answers
1. Heat is a type of energy that flows from one place to another due to differences in temperature.
2. Temperature is a measure of heat an object has.
3. Thermometer
4. Answers will vary

Possible Schedules for Week 4

Two Days a Week Schedule	
Day 1	**Day 2**
❑ Read the first page from the Heat spread (Hot and Cold) ❑ Add information about heat to the students' Narration Page ❑ Do the Scientific Demonstration: Hot Band ❑ Work on memorizing the *Energy* poem ❑ Define heat and temperature	❑ Read the second page from the Heat spread (Temperature) ❑ Add information about heat to the students' Narration Page ❑ Work on the Catapult Project ❑ Give Energy Week 4 quiz

Five Days a Week Schedule				
Day 1	**Day 2**	**Day 3**	**Day 4**	**Day 5**
❑ Do the Scientific Demonstration: Hot Band ❑ Define heat ❑ Choose one or more of the additional books to read from this week	❑ Read the first page from the Heat spread (Hot and Cold) ❑ Add information about heat to the students' Narration Page ❑ Complete the Hot or Cold Project	❑ Read the second page from the Heat spread (Temperature) ❑ Add information about heat to the students' Narration Page ❑ Complete the Heat Vibrations Project	❑ Complete the Homemade Thermometer Project ❑ Define temperature	❑ Give Energy Week 4 quiz ❑ Work on the Catapult Project
All Week Long ❑ Work on memorizing the *Energy* poem				

Week 5: Heat Transfer Lesson Plans

Scientific Demonstration: Cold Foot

Supplies Needed
- ✓ Aluminum foil
- ✓ Small throw rug or a thick towel

Purpose
This demonstration is meant to allow the students to feel the conduction of heat energy.

Instructions and Explanation
The instructions and explanation for this scientific demonstration are found on pp. 206-207 of *Janice VanCleave's Physics for Every Kid*. Have the students complete the Lab Report on SW pg. 17.

Take it Further
Have the students repeat the experiment, only this time have them fill the bathtub with warm water first and let it sit for about ten minutes so that it warms up the bottom of the tub. Then, have the students repeat the same procedure they did during the "Cold Foot" demonstration.

Science-Oriented Books

Reading Assignments
- *Usborne Science Encyclopedia pp. 112-113 Heat Transfer*
- *No pages scheduled for younger students. Instead, have the students watch the following video to learn more about heat transfer:*
  - https://www.youtube.com/watch?v=GRY6MpN2QW8
  You can also read DK Children's Encyclopedia pg. 157 Materials, which has some information about conductors.

(Optional) Additional topics to explore this week: *No additional topics scheduled.*

Discussion Questions
After reading the selected pages, ask the following questions for your discussion time.

Heat Transfer
- **?** What are the three ways that heat can be transferred?
- **?** What is convection?
- **?** What is conduction?
- **?** What is the difference between conductors and insulators?
- **?** What is radiation?
- **?** What is a vacuum?

(Optional) Additional Books
- *How Heat Moves (Science Readers)* by Sharon Coan

📖 *The Energy That Warms Us: A Look at Heat (Lightning Bolt Books)* by Jennifer Boothroyd

Notebooking

Writing Assignments

- ☐ **Narration Page** – Have the students dictate, copy, or write three to five sentences on heat transfer on SW pg. 16.
- ☐ **(Optional) Lapbook** – Have the students complete the Heat Transfer Tab-book on pp. 11-12 of *Physics for the Grammar Stage Lapbooking Templates*. Have them cut out the pages for the Tab-book and color the pictures. Then, have the students write the definition of each of the three different ways to transfer heat (convection, conduction, and radiation) on their respective pages. Once they are done, staple the mini-book together and glue it into the lapbook.
- ☐ **(Optional) Lapbook** – Have the students finish the Energy lapbook. Have them cut out and color the *Energy* poem on pg. 13 of *Physics for the Grammar Stage Lapbooking Templates*. Once they are done, have them glue the sheet into the lapbook.

Vocabulary

The following definitions are a guide. The students' definitions do not need to match word for word.

- ✎ **Conduction** – The transfer of heat through direct contact. (SW pg. 106)
- ✎ **Convection** – The transfer of heat through the movement of a liquid and gas. (SW pg. 106)
- ✎ **Radiation** – The transfer of heat through indirect contact. (SW pg. 114)

Multi-week Projects and Activities

Unit Project

- ✂ **Catapult** – This week, discuss with the students what changes they could make to improve their catapult. You can ask the following questions:
    - ❓ How would making the arm shorter or longer affect your catapult?
    - ❓ Are there ways you could add another elastic component to increase the stored energy?
    - ❓ What can you do to make a stronger base for your catapult?

    After you finish discussing these questions, have the students add a sentence or two to their catapult diary on SW pg. 7, sharing how they would change their catapult design in the future.

Projects for this Week

- ✂ **Coloring Pages** – Have the students color the following pages from *Physics for the Grammar Stage Coloring Pages*: Convection pg. 12, Conduction pg. 13.
- ✂ **Radiating Heat** – Have the students do the "See for yourself" activity on pg. 112 of the *Usborne Science Encyclopedia*. You will need a small feature and a heat source for this activity.

✂ **Water Heater –** Have the students heat up a bowl of water using radiation. You will need a sunny window sill, a bowl, and cool water. Have students fill up a bowl halfway with cool water and then set the bowl on a sunny window sill. Have them check the temperature of the water every thirty minutes and observe the changes. (*The students should see that the water heats up over time.*)

✂ **Types of Heat Transfer –** Have the students create a poster depicting the three types of heat transfer—convection, conduction, and radiation. The poster should contain the definition of the types of heat transfer plus several examples of each.

Memorization

● This week, continue working on memorizing the *Energy* poem. (SW pg. 120)

Quiz

Weekly Quiz

♪ "Energy Unit Week 5 Quiz" on SW pg. Q-9.

Quiz Answers

1. B, A, C
2. False (*A conductor transfer heat quickly, while an insulator transfers heat slowly.*)
3. True
4. Answers will vary

Possible Schedules for Week 5

Two Days a Week Schedule

Day 1	Day 2
❏ Read the first page from the Heat Transfer spread (Watch first half of the video)	❏ Read the second page from the Heat Transfer spread (Watch second half of the video)
❏ Add information about heat to the students' Narration Page	❏ Add information about heat transfer to the students' Narration Page
❏ Do the Scientific Demonstration: Cold Feet	❏ Finish the Catapult Project
❏ Work on memorizing the *Energy* poem	❏ Give Energy Week 5 quiz
❏ Define conduction, convection, and radiation	

Five Days a Week Schedule

Day 1	Day 2	Day 3	Day 4	Day 5
❏ Do the Scientific Demonstration: Cold Feet ❏ Define conduction ❏ Choose one or more of the additional books to read from this week	❏ Read the first page from the Heat Transfer spread (Watch first half of the video) ❏ Add information about heat to the students' Narration Page ❏ Complete the Radiating Heat Project	❏ Read the second page from the Heat Transfer spread (Watch second half of the video) ❏ Add information about heat to the students' Narration Page ❏ Complete the Water Heater Project	❏ Complete the Types of Heat Transfer Poster ❏ Define convection and radiation	❏ Give Energy Week 5 quiz ❏ Finish the Catapult Project

All Week Long

❏ Work on memorizing the *Energy* poem

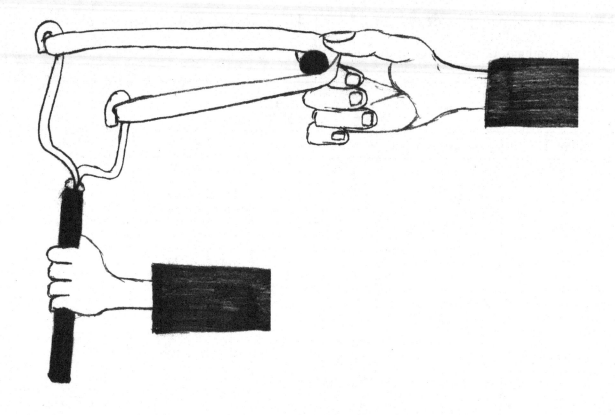

Physics for the Grammar Stage

Light Unit

Light Unit Overview
(5 weeks)

Books Scheduled

Required Encyclopedia
📖 *Usborne Science Encyclopedia*
> OR
📖 *Usborne Children's Encyclopedia* and *DK Children's Encyclopedia*

Optional Additional Encyclopedia
📖 *Basher Science Physics: Why Matter Matters!*

Scientific Demonstrations Book
📖 *JVC Physics for Every Kid*

Sequence for Study
🖰 **Week 1:** Light
🖰 **Week 2:** Color
🖰 **Week 3:** Light Behavior
🖰 **Week 4:** Lenses and Mirrors
🖰 **Week 5:** Scientist Study - Thomas Edison

Light Unit Memory Work

Colors of the Rainbow (Roy G Biv)
Red
Orange
Yellow

Green

Blue
Indigo
Violet

Light
Light is an electromagnetic wave
Rays that help us to see in a dark cave
All seven colors of visible light
The rainbow does beautifully highlight

Light hits a mirror or shiny object
Bounces back, which we say the rays reflect
Light moves from one substance to another
Rays bend, refraction will trick your brother
A curved transparent surface called a lens
Can focus light rays, on shape it depends
Focused point with concave lens, curved inward
Scattered light with convex lens, curved outward

Supplies Needed for the Unit

Week	Supplies needed
1	Small nail or screw, Box with a lid, Small objects (such as a ball, a pencil, or a toy car), Flashlight
2	Poster board, Scissors, Pencil, Ruler, Markers (red, orange, yellow, blue, green, and purple)
3	Cardboard, Flashlight, Scissors, Modeling clay, Ruler, Index card
4	Hand mirror, Pencil, Paper
5	*No supplies needed.*
Unit Project	Clear, flat plastic tote, such as the one used to store things under a bed, Wax paper, String of fluorescent rope lights, Container of salt, Squares of tissue paper in a variety of colors, Clear dish, Several different clear liquids (water, alcohol, or corn syrup), Hand mirror, Old eyeglasses or other lenses

Unit Vocabulary

1. **Light** – The electromagnetic waves of energy that make objects visible.
2. **Shadow** – A dark area that is formed when an object blocks out light waves.
3. **Primary colors** – Colors from which all other colors can be made. The primary colors are red, yellow, and blue.
4. **Secondary colors** – Colors that can be made by mixing two primary colors. The secondary colors are orange, green, and purple.
5. **Reflection** – The change in direction of light rays that occurs when it hits an object and bounces off.
6. **Refraction** – The bending of light rays caused by light passing through substances with different densities.
7. **Lens** – A curved transparent surface that causes light to bend in a particular way.
8. **Mirror** – A shiny surface that reflects nearly all the light that hits it.

Week 1: Light Lesson Plans

Scientific Demonstration: Sight Box

Supplies Needed
- ✓ Small nail or screw
- ✓ Box with a lid
- ✓ Small objects, such as a ball, a pencil, or a toy car
- ✓ Flashlight

Purpose
This demonstration is meant to help the students see how light allows us to see objects.

Instructions
1. Use a small nail or screw to make a pin hole at the end of one side of the box.
2. Place the small objects inside the box and then close the lid tightly. Ask the students to come and look inside the hole to see what is in the box.
3. Then, have the students step back as you turn on the flashlight. Place the flashlight in the box opposite from the objects. Ask the students to come and look inside the hole again to see what is in the box.
4. Have the students complete the Lab Report on SW pg. 23.

Explanation
The students should not be able to see the objects when the cover is on, and they should be able to see the objects when the flashlight is on. We see objects because light bounces off the objects and is reflected back to our eyes, letting our brain know that something is there. If there is no source of light, we cannot see the objects that are there.

Take it Further
Open the box lid and have the students look in the hole once more. This time, have them look for the shadows that are created by the objects. (*All opaque objects create shadows because light waves cannot pass through the objects. The presence and angle of the shadow depends upon the direction of the light as it hits the objects.*)

Science-Oriented Books

Reading Assignments
- 📖 *Usborne Science Encyclopedia pp. 214-215 Light and Shadow*
- 📖 *Usborne Children's Encyclopedia pp. 206-207 Light and color, DK Children's Encyclopedia pg. 147 Light*

(Optional) Additional topics to explore this week: *Basher Physics pg. 68 Light*

Discussion Questions
After reading the selected pages, ask the following questions for your discussion time.

Light
? What is light?

? What is a luminous object?

? Why does a shadow form?

? How does a simple laser work?

? What are fluorescent objects able to do?

(Optional) Additional Books

- *Light Is All Around Us (Let's-Read-and-Find-Out Science 2)* by Wendy Pfeffer and Paul Meisel
- *All About Light (Rookie Read-About Science)* by Lisa Trumbauer
- *Day Light, Night Light: Where Light Comes From (Let's-Read-and-Find-Out Science 2)* by Dr. Franklyn M. Branley and Stacey Schuett

Notebooking

Writing Assignments

☐ **Narration Page** – Have the students dictate, copy, or write three to five sentences about light on SW pg. 22. For example, this week the students could dictate, copy, or write the following:

> *Light is a form of energy made of electromagnetic waves. Luminous objects give*
> *off light. All opaque objects have shadows because light cannot pass through them.*
> *A simple laser absorbs light energy and gives if off in short bursts.*
> *Fluorescent objects are able to absorb electricity or ultraviolet rays and give it out as light.*

☐ **(Optional) Lapbook** – Have the students begin the Light and Sound lapbook by cutting out and coloring the cover on pg. 15. Then, have the students glue the sheet onto the front. (**Note**—*The students will work on this lapbook through this unit and the next.*)

☐ **(Optional) Lapbook** – Have the students complete the Light vs. Shadow Shutterfold book on pg. 16 of *Physics for the Grammar Stage Lapbooking Templates*. Have them cut out and fold the template. Have the students color the pictures on the cover. Then, have the students write the definition of light under the light flap and the definition of shadow under the shadow flap. Finally, have them glue the mini-book into the lapbook.

Vocabulary

The following definitions are a guide. The students' definitions do not need to match word for word.

✎ **Light** – The electromagnetic waves of energy that make objects visible. (SW pg. 110)

✎ **Shadow** – A dark area that is formed when an object blocks out light waves. (SW pg. 116)

Multi-week Projects and Activities

Unit Project

✂ **Light Box** – For this unit, the students will be playing and learning about light using a light box. This week, you will be assembling the light box and testing it out. You will need a clear, flat plastic tote, such as the one used to store things under a bed, wax paper, a string of fluorescent rope lights, and a container of salt. Cover the underside of the tote's lid with the wax paper and place the string of light inside the tote. Secure the lid, leaving a bit of room around one of the edges for the cord from the string of lights to hang out so you can plug it in. Have the students pour a thin layer of salt on the lid so that it covers the lid, but doesn't spill out over the slight lip. Then, turn on the lights and let the students use their fingers to create designs. Lead them to create transparent, translucent, and opaque places on the lid. Take a picture and add the photo along with a sentence or two of what they learned to the Light Box Diary on SW pg. 20. When they are done, throw away the salt and store the box for next week.

Projects for this Week

✂ **Coloring Pages** – Have the students color the following pages from *Physics for the Grammar Stage Coloring Pages*: Light pg. 14, Shadow pg. 15.

✂ **Light Camera** – Have the students make a pinhole camera. You will need a round oatmeal container, tissue paper, aluminum foil, a pin, a knife, tape, black construction paper, and a flashlight. Remove the top of the oatmeal container, cover it with tissue paper, and use tape to secure it in place. Then, flip it upside down and cut a small square in the bottom of the container. Cover this hole with foil and use tape to secure it in place. Next, use the pin to make a small hole in the center of the foil. After that, cut a small shape, such as a triangle or small paper doll, out of the construction paper. Now, take all that you have made into a darkened room. Set up the box about two feet from the flashlight, so that the flashlight is pointed towards the pinhole in the bottom of the oatmeal container. Turn the flashlight on and put the black construction paper shape in front of the flashlight, about an inch or so away from the flashlight. Then, have the students look at the tissue paper covering the top of the oatmeal container to observe what they see. (*The students should see the image of their shape upside down. This is because the light travels straight from the top and bottom of the object at an angle and causes the image to be flipped, just like it does in our eyes, and then our brain turns the image right side up again.*)

✂ **Shadows** – Have the students do the "See for yourself" activity on pg. 214 of the *Usborne Science Encyclopedia*. You will need a light source and a book for this activity.

✂ **Light Poster** – Have the students make a poster about transparent, translucent, and opaque objects. You will need poster board, colored yarn, glue plastic wrap, wax paper, white construction paper, tape, and a maker. Divide the poster into three sections and label one section "transparent," one section "translucent," and the last section "opaque." Next, glue the piece of yarn so that it runs the full length of the poster, through the middle of all three sections. Finally, cover the yarn with plastic wrap under the transparent section, cover the yarn with wax paper under the translucent section, and cover the yarn with construction paper under the opaque section. (*The student should see that the yarn is visible under the transparent section, the yarn is semi-visible under the translucent section, and the yarn is not visible at all under the opaque section.*)

Memorization

🖌 This week, begin working on memorizing the *Colors of the Rainbow*. (SW pg. 121)

Quiz

Weekly Quiz
- "Light Unit Week 1 Quiz" on SW pg. Q-10.

Quiz Answers
1. True
2. Opaque
3. B, C, A
2. Answers will vary

Possible Schedules for Week 1

Two Days a Week Schedule	
Day 1	**Day 2**
❑ Read the first page from the Light and Shadow spread (Light and Color) ❑ Add information about light and shadows to the students' Narration Page ❑ Do the Scientific Demonstration: Light Box ❑ Define light and shadow	❑ Read the second page from the Light and Shadow spread (Light) ❑ Add information about lasers and fluorescence to the students' Narration Page ❑ Work on memorizing the *Colors of the Rainbow* and work on the Light Box Project ❑ Give Light Week 1 quiz

Five Days a Week Schedule				
Day 1	**Day 2**	**Day 3**	**Day 4**	**Day 5**
❑ Do the Scientific Demonstration: Light Box ❑ Define light and shadow ❑ Choose one or more of the additional books to read from this week	❑ Read the first page from the Light and Shadow spread (Light and Color) ❑ Add information about light and shadows to the students' Narration Page ❑ Complete the Light Project	❑ Read the second page from the Light and Shadow spread (Light) ❑ Add information about lasers and fluorescence to the students' Narration Page ❑ Complete the Shadows Project	❑ Complete the Light Poster Project ❑ Choose one or more of the additional books to read from this week	❑ Give Light Week 1 quiz ❑ Work on the Light Box Project
All Week Long				
❑ Work on memorizing the *Colors of the Rainbow*				

Week 2: Colors Lesson Plans

Scientific Demonstration: Blender

Supplies Needed
- ✓ Poster board
- ✓ Scissors
- ✓ Pencil
- ✓ Ruler
- ✓ Markers (red, orange, yellow, blue, green, and purple)

Purpose
This demonstration is meant to help the students see how light waves blend together.

Instructions and Explanation
The instructions and explanation for this scientific demonstration are found on pp. 190-191 of *Janice VanCleave's Physics for Every Kid*. Have the students complete the Lab Report on SW pg. 25.

Take it Further
Have the students do another color-related demonstration - "Swirls of Color" on pp. 186-187 of *Janice VanCleave's Physics for Every Kid*.

Science-Oriented Books

Reading Assignments
- 📖 *Usborne Science Encyclopedia pp. 216-217 Color*
- 📖 *DK Children's Encyclopedia pp. 26-27 Color*

(Optional) Additional topics to explore this week: *No pages scheduled.*

Discussion Questions
After reading the selected pages, ask the following questions for your discussion time.

Color
- **?** What are the seven colors that make up visible light?
- **?** What makes each color different?
- **?** What is dispersion?
- **?** What are the primary colors? Secondary colors?
- **?** How do we see color?

(Optional) Additional Books
- 📖 *Pantone: Colors* by Pantone and Helen Dardik
- 📖 *All the Colors of the Rainbow (Rookie Read-About Science)* by Allan Fowler
- 📖 *Color Day Relay (The Magic School Bus Chapter Book)* by Gail Herman and Hope Gangloff

Notebooking

Writing Assignments

- ☐ **Narration Page –** Have the students dictate, copy, or write three to five sentences on color on SW pg. 24.
- ☐ **(Optional) Lapbook –** Have the students complete the Colors Tab-book on pg. 17 of *Physics for the Grammar Stage Lapbooking Templates*. Have them cut out the pages for the tab-book and color the pictures. Then, have the students add a sentence about primary colors, along with the colors that are considered primary colors, on the primary page. Have them add a sentence about secondary colors, along with the colors that are considered secondary colors, on the secondary page. Assemble the tab-book and staple it together on the dashed lines. Finally, have the students glue the mini-book into the lapbook.

Vocabulary

The following definitions are a guide. The students' definitions do not need to match word for word.

- ✐ **Primary colors –** Colors from which all other colors can be made. The primary colors are red, yellow, and blue. (SW pg. 113)
- ✐ **Secondary colors –** Colors that can be made by mixing two primary colors. The secondary colors are orange, green, and purple. (SW pg. 115)

Multi-week Projects and Activities

Unit Project

- ✂ **Light Box –** This week, have the students use their light box from last week to explore color. You will need tissue paper squares in a variety of colors. Have the students lay out the items on the light box lid and turn on the lights. Let them move the paper squares around, overlapping them to see what happens. Have the students take a picture and write down their observations on SW pg. 20.

Projects for this Week

- ✂ **Coloring Pages –** Have the students color the following pages from *Physics for the Grammar Stage Coloring Pages*: The Color Wheel pg. 16.
- ✂ **Color Mixing –** Have the students create a color wheel by mixing paint. You will need a piece of paper, paint (red, yellow, and blue), pencil, and a paintbrush. Draw a circle and divide it into six parts. Begin with the primary colors by painting one part red and skip the next section. Repeat this process for both the yellow and blue. Then, add the secondary colors by mixing the two surrounding primary colors in the blank section, i.e., if the blank section is in between red and yellow, mix red and yellow to make orange. Repeat the process until the wheel has all the primary and secondary colors.
- ✂ **Up-close Color –** Have the students look at a printed color cover or page up close,

using a magnifying glass. (*Note – You can get better results for this activity with either a currency detection scope or a microscope.*)

✂ **Milky Colors –** Have the students observe color mixing in milk. You will need a shallow dish, milk, liquid soap, and red, yellow, and blue food coloring. Fill the dish with a layer of milk. Drop several drops of the different colors of food coloring at different places along the edge of the dish. Then, add a drop or two of liquid dish soap to the center of the bowl and observe what happens. (*Within moments, the dish soap will break the surface tension of the milk and the colors will begin to swirl and mix in the bowl.*)

Memorization

● This week, continue working on memorizing the *Colors of the Rainbow*. (SW pg. 121)

Quiz

Weekly Quiz
⚲ "Light Unit Week 2 Quiz" on SW pg. Q-11.

Quiz Answers
1. Red, Orange, Yellow, Green, Blue, Indigo, Violet
2. False (*Different colors have different wavelengths and frequencies.*)
3. Answers will vary

Possible Schedules for Week 2

Two Days a Week Schedule

Day 1	Day 2
❏ Read the first page from the Color spread	❏ Read the second page from the Color spread
❏ Add information about color to the students' Narration Page	❏ Add information about color to the students' Narration Page
❏ Do the Scientific Demonstration: Blender	❏ Work on the Light Box Project
❏ Work on memorizing the *Colors of the Rainbow* poem	❏ Give Light Week 2 quiz
❏ Define primary and secondary colors	

Five Days a Week Schedule

Day 1	Day 2	Day 3	Day 4	Day 5
❏ Do the Scientific Demonstration: Blender ❏ Define primary and secondary colors ❏ Choose one or more of the additional books to read from this week	❏ Read the first page from the Color spread ❏ Add information about color to the students' Narration Page ❏ Complete the Color Mixing Project	❏ Read the second page from the Color spread ❏ Add information about color to the students' Narration Page ❏ Complete the Up-close Color Project	❏ Complete the Milky Colors Project ❏ Choose one or more of the additional books to read from this week	❏ Give Light Week 2 quiz ❏ Work on the Light Box Project

All Week Long

❏ Work on memorizing the *Energy* poem

Week 3: Light Behavior Lesson Plans

Scientific Demonstration: Straight

Supplies Needed
- ✓ Cardboard
- ✓ Flashlight
- ✓ Scissors
- ✓ Modeling clay
- ✓ Ruler
- ✓ Index card

Purpose
This demonstration is meant to help the students see how light travels.

Instructions and Explanation
The instructions and explanation for this scientific demonstration are found on pp. 180-181 of *Janice VanCleave's Physics for Every Kid*. Have the students complete the Lab Report on SW pg. 27.

Take it Further
Have the students do another light-related demonstration - "See-through" on pp. 182-183 of *Janice VanCleave's Physics for Every Kid*.

Science-Oriented Books

Reading Assignments
- 📖 *Usborne Science Encyclopedia pp. 218-219 Light Behavior*
- 📖 *No pages are scheduled for younger students. Instead, have the students watch the following video to learn more about light behavior:*
  - 🖱 https://www.youtube.com/watch?v=JRh0CGfX7dQ

(Optional) Additional topics to explore this week: *No additional pages scheduled.*

Discussion Questions
After reading the selected pages, ask the following questions for your discussion time.

Light Behavior
- ? What are light rays?
- ? What happens when light is reflected?
- ? What happens when light is refracted?
- ? What happens when light is diffracted?
- ? What causes iridescence?
- ? How do polarized sunglasses work?

(Optional) Additional Books
- 📖 *Shadows and Reflections (Light All Around Us)* by Daniel Nunn

📖 *Shadows and Reflections* by Tana Hoban
📖 *What Are Shadows and Reflections? (Light & Sound Waves Close-Up)* by Robin Johnson

Notebooking

Writing Assignments

☐ **Narration Page –** Have the students dictate, copy, or write three to five sentences on light behavior on SW pg. 26.

☐ **(Optional) Lapbook –** Have the students complete the Light Behavior Triangle Book on pg. 18 of *Physics for the Grammar Stage Lapbooking Templates*. Have them cut out the pages for the triangle book and color the pictures. Then, have the students add a sentence about reflection, refraction, and diffraction on the respective flaps. Assemble the triangle book and glue on the cover for the mini-book. Finally, have the students glue the mini-book into the lapbook.

Vocabulary

The following definitions are a guide. The students' definitions do not need to match word for word.

✎ **Reflection –** The change in direction of light rays that occurs when it hits an object and bounces off. (SW pg. 114)

✎ **Refraction –** The bending of light rays caused by light passing through substances with different densities. (SW pg. 114)

Multi-week Projects and Activities

Unit Project

✂ **Light Box –** This week, have the students use their light box to learn about refraction. You will need the tissue paper squares from last week, along with a clear dish and several different clear liquids, such as water, alcohol, and corn syrup. Have the students lay out the colored squares across the top of the light box lid as you fill the clear dish halfway with one of the clear liquids. Then, place the dish on top of the squares and observe what happens. Have the students repeat this process for the other clear liquids you selected. After they finish, have them take a picture and add their observations to SW pg. 21.

Projects for this Week

✂ **Coloring Pages –** Have the students color the following pages from *Physics for the Grammar Stage Coloring Pages*: Reflection pg. 17, Refraction pg. 18.

✂ **Reflection –** Have the students use a homemade kaleidoscope to see reflection in action. You will need an empty toilet paper roll, a thick mylar sheet, scissors, tape, cardstock, a straw, and markers. Find the directions for this activity here:
🖱 https://buggyandbuddy.com/science-for-kids-how-to-make-a-kaleidoscope/

✂ **Refraction –** Have the students do the "See for yourself" activity on pg. 218 of the *Usborne*

Science Encyclopedia. You will need a glass of water and a straw for this activity.

✂ **Iridescence –** Have the students see iridescence using soap bubbles. You will need a container of bubbles and a glass plate. Have the students blow a few bubbles on the glass plate. Then, have them observe the colors as light hits the bubbles. (*The students should see the colors of the rainbow all over the bubbles. The colors will change as well, making the bubbles appear to shimmer. This is because soap bubbles are basically a thin layer of water trapped in between two thin layers of soap. Part of the light rays are reflection off the outer layer and part of the light rays are reflection off the inner layer. This effect causes the light rays to travel differently, meaning that our eyes "see" the light as different colors.*)

Memorization

🕴 This week, begin working on memorizing the *Light* poem. (SW pg. 121)

Quiz

Weekly Quiz

🕯 "Light Unit Week 3 Quiz" on SW pg. Q-12.

Quiz Answers

1. When light is reflected, the rays hit an object and bounce off it.
2. When light is refracted, the rays are bent as they pass from one substance through another one of differing density. (**Note**—*If your students have only noted that the rays are bent, you can mark this answer correct.*)
3. True
4. Answers will vary

Possible Schedules for Week 3

Two Days a Week Schedule	
Day 1	**Day 2**
❑ Read the first page from the Light Behavior spread (Watch the first half of the video) ❑ Add information about light behavior to the students' Narration Page ❑ Do the Scientific Demonstration: Straight ❑ Work on memorizing the *Light* poem ❑ Define reflection and refraction	❑ Read the second page from the Light Behavior spread (Watch the second half of the video) ❑ Add information about light behavior to the students' Narration Page ❑ Work on the Light Box Project ❑ Give Light Week 3 quiz

Five Days a Week Schedule				
Day 1	**Day 2**	**Day 3**	**Day 4**	**Day 5**
❑ Do the Scientific Demonstration: Straight ❑ Define reflection and refraction ❑ Choose one or more of the additional books to read from this week	❑ Read the first page from the Light Behavior spread (Watch the first half of the video) ❑ Add information about light behavior to the students' Narration Page ❑ Complete the Reflection Project	❑ Read the second page from the Light Behavior spread (Watch the second half of the video) ❑ Add information about light behavior to the students' Narration Page ❑ Complete the Refraction Project	❑ Complete the Iridesence Project ❑ Choose one or more of the additional books to read from this week	❑ Give Light Week 3 quiz ❑ Work on the Light Box Project
All Week Long				
❑ Work on memorizing the *Light* poem				

Week 4: Lenses and Mirrors Lesson Plans

Scientific Demonstration: Backwards

Supplies Needed
- ✓ Hand mirror
- ✓ Pencil
- ✓ Paper

Purpose
This demonstration is meant to help the students see and feel energy changes.

Instructions and Explanation
The instructions and explanation for this scientific demonstration are found on pp. 194-195 of *Janice VanCleave's Physics for Every Kid*. Have the students complete the Lab Report on SW pg. 29.

Take it Further
Have the students do another lens-related demonstration - "Polarized Light" on pp. 184-185 of *Janice VanCleave's Physics for Every Kid*.

Science-Oriented Books

Reading Assignments
- 📖 *Usborne Science Encyclopedia pp. 220-221 Lens and Mirrors*
- 📖 *No pages are scheduled for younger students. Instead, have the students watch the following video to learn more about lens and mirrors:*
  - 🖱 Convex lens - https://www.youtube.com/watch?v=cf_aUBbyuts
  - 🖱 Mirror - https://www.youtube.com/watch?v=N6n0FAZ_6N8

(Optional) Additional topics to explore this week: *No additional topics scheduled.*

Discussion Questions
After reading the selected pages, ask the following questions for your discussion time.

Lenses and Mirrors
- **?** What is a lens?
- **?** What is a convex lens? Concave lens?
- **?** What is the difference between converging and diverging lenses?
- **?** What type of lens does our eye have?
- **?** What is a mirror?

(Optional) Additional Books
- 📖 *Light: Shadows, Mirrors, and Rainbows (Amazing Science)* by Natalie M. Rosinsky and Sheree Boyd

Notebooking

Writing Assignments

- ☐ **Narration Page –** Have the students dictate, copy, or write three to five sentences on lenses and mirrors on SW pg. 28.
- ☐ **(Optional) Lapbook –** Have the students complete the Lenses and Mirrors Mini-book on pg. 19 of *Physics for the Grammar Stage Lapbooking Templates*. Have them cut out and fold the template. Have the students color the pictures on the cover. Then, have the students write the difference between lenses and mirrors on the inside. Finally, have them glue the mini-book into the lapbook.

Vocabulary

The following definitions are a guide. The students' definitions do not need to match word for word.

- ✎ **Lens –** A curved transparent surface that causes light to bend in a particular way. (SW pg. 110)
- ✎ **Mirror –** A shiny surface that reflects nearly all the light that hits it. (SW pg. 112)

Multi-week Projects and Activities

Unit Project

- ✂ **Light Box –** This week, have the students use their light box to learn more about lenses and mirrors. You will need a hand mirror and a pair of old eyeglasses or other lenses. Have the students use the mirror and lenses to see how the light passes through (or reflects off) these surfaces. After they finish, have them take a picture and add their observations to SW pg. 21.

Projects for this Week

- ✂ **Coloring Pages –** Have the students color the following pages from *Physics for the Grammar Stage Coloring Pages*: Lenses pg 19.
- ✂ **Glass Lens –** Have the students make their own reading "glasses." You will need a glass jar, water, pencil, and an index card. Have the students fill the glass jar with water as you write a message on the index card in very small letters. Then, have the students hold the index card up to the jar so that they are looking through the jar to read the card. Have them read your message aloud. (*They should see that the message appears larger as the curved glass jar and water serve as a magnifying glass.*)
- ✂ **Reflections –** Have the students do the "See for yourself" activity on pg. 221 of the *Usborne Science Encyclopedia*. You will need a metal spoon for this activity.
- ✂ **Mirrorscope –** Have the students make their own periscope. You will need two mirrors of the same size, cardboard, a ruler, and a hot glue gun. Watch the following video for directions on how to make a homemade periscope:
  - 🖱 https://www.youtube.com/watch?v=F_j_BkYcF4c

Memorization

🗣 This week, continue working on memorizing the *Light* poem. (SW pg. 121)

Quiz

Weekly Quiz

🖊 "Light Unit Week 4 Quiz" on SW pg. Q-13.

Quiz Answers

1. False (*A lens is a curved transparent surface that causes light to bend in a particular way.*)
2. False (*A mirror is a shiny surface that reflects nearly all the light that hits it.*)
3. In a concave lens, one or both sides curve inward. In a convex lens, one or both sides curve outward.
4. True
5. Answers will vary

Possible Schedules for Week 4

Two Days a Week Schedule	
Day 1	**Day 2**
❑ Read the first page from the Lenses and Mirrors spread (Watch convex lens video) ❑ Add information about lenses to the students' Narration Page ❑ Do the Scientific Demonstration: Backwards ❑ Work on memorizing the *Light* poem ❑ Define lens and mirror	❑ Read the first page from the Lenses and Mirrors spread (Watch the mirror video) ❑ Add information about mirrors to the students' Narration Page ❑ Work on the Light Box Project ❑ Give Light Week 4 quiz

Five Days a Week Schedule				
Day 1	**Day 2**	**Day 3**	**Day 4**	**Day 5**
❑ Do the Scientific Demonstration: Backwards ❑ Define lens and mirror ❑ Choose one or more of the additional books to read from this week	❑ Read the first page from the Lenses and Mirrors spread (Watch convex lens video) ❑ Add information about lenses to the students' Narration Page ❑ Complete the Glass Lens Project	❑ Read the first page from the Lenses and Mirrors spread (Watch the mirror video) ❑ Add information about mirrors to the students' Narration Page ❑ Complete the Reflections Project	❑ Complete the Mirrorscope Project ❑ Choose one or more of the additional books to read from this week	❑ Give Light Week 4 quiz ❑ Work on the Light Box Project
All Week Long				
❑ Work on memorizing the *Light* poem				

Week 5: Scientist Study - Thomas Edison

Science-Oriented Books

Reading Assignments

📖 *Who Was Thomas Alva Edison?* by Margaret Frith

Over this week, the students will be reading *Who Was Thomas Alva Edison?* You can purchase this book or you can get another book from the library. If you choose to get a different biography from the library, here are a few options:

📖 *National Geographic Readers: Thomas Edison (Readers Bios)* by Barbara Kramer
📖 *A Wizard from the Start: The Incredible Boyhood and Amazing Inventions of Thomas Edison* by Don Brown
📖 *Thomas Edison: The Great Inventor (DK Readers)* by Caryn Jenner

If you cannot find a suitable book on Thomas Edison at your library, you could look for a biography on one of the following scientists:

1. Isaac Newton - He founded the laws of gravity and motion.
2. Albert Einstein - He discovered $E=mc^2$, plus many other theories.
3. Niels Bohr - He applied quantum theory of physics to the structure of the atom.
4. William Gilbert - He was an English physicist who founded the study of magnetism.
5. Lord Kelvin (William Thomson) - He established the absolute temperature scale.

Assign the reading according to each student's skill level. In other words, if the students need two weeks to read the biography, take the extra time by moving the following weeks back and eliminating the additional biography assignment.

Discussion Questions

After reading the selected pages from the encyclopedias, ask the following questions in your discussion time:

? What was the title of the book you read?
? When and where was Thomas Edison born?
? What was his major scientific contribution?
? List the events that surround his discovery.
? List some other interesting events in the his life.
? Why do you think it is important to learn about Thomas Edison?

Notebooking

Writing Assignments

☐ **Scientist Questionnaire –** Have the students fill in their answers to the questions about Thomas Edison on SW pp. 30-31.

☐ **(Optional) Scientist Report –** If you have older students, you may opt to have them write a short report on Thomas Edison. Have the students use their responses on the scientist questionnaire to write their rough draft. It should include an introductory paragraph, a paragraph on his scientific contributions, a paragraph on other interesting events in the scientist's life, and a conclusion that includes why they feel it is important to study that particular scientist. Have the students proofread and correct mistakes. Finally, have them give their reports a title and rewrite them as a final draft. Here are a few ideas to make their reports a bit more interesting:

1. Have the students turn their reports into a mini-book on the scientist, including pictures they have drawn.
2. Have the students make posters to present their reports.

Quiz

Weekly Quiz
↟ "Light Unit Week 5 Quiz" on SW pg. Q-14.

Quiz Answers
1. Answers will vary

Physics for the Grammar Stage

Sound Unit

Sound Unit Overview
(4 weeks)

Books Scheduled

Required Encyclopedia

📖 *Usborne Science Encyclopedia*

OR

📖 *Usborne Children's Encyclopedia* and *DK Children's Encyclopedia*

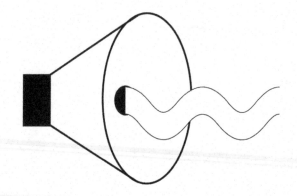

Optional Additional Encyclopedia

📖 *Basher Science Physics: Why Matter Matters!*

Scientific Demonstrations Book

📖 *JVC Physics for Every Kid*

Sequence for Study

↻ **Week 1:** Sound
↻ **Week 2:** Waves
↻ **Week 3:** Wave Behavior
↻ **Week 4:** Musical Instruments

Sound Unit Memory Work

Sound

Sound is energy we can hear
Waves that are captured by an ear

Something vibrates and sound waves start
Instruments make sound a fine art

Some sound is soft, some sound is loud
Decibels gauge sound in a crowd

When sound waves meet, changes appear
Waves mix and build or disappear.

Supplies Needed for the Unit

Week	Supplies needed
1	Stemmed glassware, Liquid soap, Vinegar
2	Ruler, Table
3	Cup, Rubber band
4	Straw, Scissors, Ruler, Marking pen
Unit Project	*Materials will vary based on the instrument you choose to make.*

Unit Vocabulary

1. **Decibel (dB) –** The unit of loudness.
2. **Sound Wave –** A mechanical wave that carries sound energy through a medium.
3. **Longitudinal Wave –** A wave that vibrates in the same direction as it travels.
4. **Transverse Wave –** A wave that vibrates at right angles to the direction of travel.
5. **Interference –** The effect that occurs when two waves meet.
6. **Resonate –** To vibrate at the same frequency as something else.

Week 1: Sound Lesson Plans

Scientific Demonstration: Singing Glass

Supplies Needed
- ✓ Stemmed glassware
- ✓ Liquid soap
- ✓ Vinegar

Purpose
This demonstration is meant to help the students see how friction can cause a glass to vibrate and produce a sound.

Instructions and Explanation
The instructions and explanation for this scientific demonstration are found on pp. 218-219 of *Janice VanCleave's Physics for Every Kid*. Have the students complete the Lab Report on SW pg. 37.

Take it Further
Have the students do another sound-related demonstration - "Bottle Organ" on pp. 216-217 of *Janice VanCleave's Physics for Every Kid*.

Science-Oriented Books

Reading Assignments
- 📖 *Usborne Science Encyclopedia pp. 206-207 Sound*
- 📖 *Usborne Children's Encyclopedia pg. 208 Sound, DK Children's Encyclopedia pg. 235 Sound*

(Optional) Additional topics to explore this week: *Basher Physics pg. 46 Sound*

Discussion Questions
After reading the selected pages, ask the following questions for your discussion time.

Sound
- **?** What is sound?
- **?** What substances can sound travel through? What can sound not travel through?
- **?** What happens to sound as it travels farther from the source?
- **?** What is an echo?

(Optional) Additional Books
- 📖 *Sound: Loud, Soft, High, and Low (Amazing Science)* by Natalie M. Rosinsky and Matthew John
- 📖 *Sounds All Around (Let's-Read-and-Find-Out Science 1)* by Wendy Pfeffer and Anna Chernyshova
- 📖 *All About Sound (Rookie Read-About Science)* by Lisa Trumbauer

Notebooking

Writing Assignments
- 📓 **Narration Page –** Have the students dictate, copy, or write three to five sentences about

sound on SW pg. 36. For example, this week the students could dictate, copy, or write the following:

> *Sound is a form of energy carried by waves. These waves can travel through*
> *solids, liquids, or gases, but they cannot travel through a vacuum.*
> *As you get farther away from the source of a sound wave, the loudness of the sound goes down.*
> *An echo happens when sound waves are reflected off a hard surface and bounce back.*

☐ **(Optional) Lapbook –** Have the students complete the Sound Mini-book on pg. 20 of *Physics for the Grammar Stage Lapbooking Templates.* Have them cut out and fold the template. Have the students color the pictures on the cover. Then, have the students write the definition of sound inside the mini-book. Finally, have them glue the mini-book into the lapbook.

Vocabulary

The following definitions are a guide. The students' definitions do not need to match word for word.

✎ **Decibel (dB) –** The unit of loudness. (SW pg. 106)

✎ **Sound Wave –** A mechanical wave that carries sound energy through a medium.(SW pg. 116)

Multi-week Projects and Activities

Unit Project

✂ **Homemade Sound –** For this unit, the students will make a new homemade instrument each week. Choose from one of the projects below:

  ✌ **PVC Pipe Xylophone:** https://frugalfun4boys.com/2015/03/18/how-to-make-pvc-pipe-xylophone-instrument/

  ✌ **Straw Flute:** http://krokotak.com/2013/04/singing-straws/

  ✌ **Pringle's Can Drums:** https://www.thetaylor-house.com/upcycled-pringles-can-diy-drum/

  ✌ **Homemade French Horn:** https://www.savvyhomemade.com/homemade-french-horn-for-kids/

  ✌ **Popsicle Stick Harmonica:** http://www.housingaforest.com/popsicle-stick-harmonica/

  ✌ **Cardboard Guitar:** http://www.minieco.co.uk/cardboard-instruments/

Once the students have completed the project, have them take a picture and add it to their unit project sheet on SW pg. 34.

Projects for this Week

✂ **Coloring Pages –** Have the students color the following pages from *Physics for the Grammar Stage Coloring Pages*: Sound pg. 20.

✂ **Sound –** Have the students feel the vibrations that sound makes. Have them place a hand lightly on their neck and then begin to hum or sing. (*The students should feel the vibrations in their throat. This is because our vocal cords vibrate to produce sound that can be heard.*)

✂ **Echo Game** – Have the students play a game of echolocation, otherwise known as Marco Polo. Choose one person to be "it" and blindfold that person. (*Be sure that you are playing this game in a location free from trip-hazards.*) To begin the game, the blindfolded player cries out "Marco" and the other players respond with "Polo." The blindfolded player then tries to tag another player based on where he or she heard them. When the blindfolded player finally tags someone, that person becomes the next blindfolded Marco.

✂ **Sound Vibrations** – Have the students do the "See for yourself" activity on pg. 206 of the *Usborne Science Encyclopedia*. You will need a speaker and a balloon for this activity.

Memorization

🗣 This week, begin working on memorizing the *Sound* Poem. (SW pg. 122)

Quiz

Weekly Quiz

🔊 "Sound Unit Week 1 Quiz" on SW pg. Q-15.

Quiz Answers

1. True
2. There are lots of options to answer, but the two most common are air and water. As long as the student answers include some type of solid, liquid, or gas, count their response as correct.
3. A vacuum
4. False (*An echo of a sound wave can be used to determine position.*)
5. Answers will vary

Possible Schedules for Week 1

Two Days a Week Schedule	
Day 1	**Day 2**
❑ Read the first page from the Sound spread (Sound from the Usborne book)	❑ Read the second page from the Sound spread (Sound from the DK book)
❑ Add information about sound to the students' Narration Page	❑ Add information about echoes to the students' Narration Page
❑ Do the Scientific Demonstration: Singing Glass	❑ Work on memorizing the *Sound Poem* and work on the Homemade Sound Project
❑ Define decibel and sound wave	❑ Give Sound Week 1 quiz

Five Days a Week Schedule				
Day 1	**Day 2**	**Day 3**	**Day 4**	**Day 5**
❑ Do the Scientific Demonstration: Singing Glass ❑ Define decibel and sound wave ❑ Choose one or more of the additional books to read from this week	❑ Read the first page from the Sound spread (Sound from the Usborne book) ❑ Add information about sound to the students' Narration Page ❑ Complete the Sound Project	❑ Read the second page from the Sound spread (Sound from the DK book) ❑ Add information about echoes to the students' Narration Page ❑ Complete the Echo Game Project	❑ Complete the Sound Vibrations Project ❑ Choose one or more of the additional books to read from this week	❑ Give Sound Week 1 quiz ❑ Work on the Homemade Sound Project
All Week Long				
❑ Work on memorizing the *Sound Poem*				

Week 2: Waves Lesson Plans

Scientific Demonstration: Twang

Supplies Needed
- ✓ Ruler
- ✓ Table

Purpose
This demonstration is meant to help the students see how length affects sound vibrations.

Instructions and Explanation
The instructions and explanation for this scientific demonstration are found on pp. 222-223 of *Janice VanCleave's Physics for Every Kid*. Have the students complete the Lab Report on SW pg. 39.

Take it Further
Have the students do another sound-vibration-related demonstration - "Clucking Chicken" on pp. 226-227 of *Janice VanCleave's Physics for Every Kid*.

Science-Oriented Books

Reading Assignments
- 📖 *Usborne Science Encyclopedia pp. 202-203 Waves*
- 📖 *No pages are scheduled for younger students. Instead, have the students watch the following video to learn more about the two types of waves:*
  - 🖱 https://www.youtube.com/watch?v=RVyHkV3wIyk

(Optional) Additional topics to explore this week: *Basher Physics pg. 42 (Wave Gang), Usborne Children's Encyclopedia pp. 36-37 (Waves-water)*

Discussion Questions
After reading the selected pages, ask the following questions for your discussion time.

Waves
- **?** What do waves carry?
- **?** What are mechanical waves?
- **?** What are transverse waves? Longitudinal waves?
- **?** What are the high points of a wave called? Low points?

(Optional) Additional Books
- 📖 *Sound Waves and Communication (Science Readers)* by Jenna Winterberg
- 📖 *What Are Sound Waves? (Light & Sound Waves Close-Up)* by Robin Johnson
- 📖 *Sound Waves (Energy in Action)* by Ian F. Mahaney
- 📖 *The Science of Sound Waves (Catch a Wave)* by Robin Johnson

Notebooking

Writing Assignments

- ☐ **Narration Page** – Have the students dictate, copy, or write three to five sentences on waves on SW pg. 38.
- ☐ **(Optional) Lapbook** – Have the students complete the Waves Shutterfold-book on pg. 21 of *Physics for the Grammar Stage Lapbooking Templates*. Have them cut out the mini-book template and color the pictures. Then, have the students add a sentence about longitudinal waves under the picture of the longitudinal wave (upper) and a sentence about transverse waves under the picture of the transverse wave (lower.) Finally, fold the mini-book along dashed lines and have the students glue the mini-book into the lapbook.

Vocabulary

The following definitions are a guide. The students' definitions do not need to match word for word.

- ✎ **Longitudinal Wave** – A wave that vibrates in the same direction as it travels. (SW pg. 111)
- ✎ **Transverse Wave** – A wave that vibrates at right angles to the direction of travel. (SW pg. 117)

Multi-week Projects and Activities

Unit Project

- ✂ **Homemade Sound** – This week, have the students continue to add to their suite of homemade instruments. Choose one of the projects from the list below that you have not already done:
  - 👆 **PVC Pipe Xylophone:** https://frugalfun4boys.com/2015/03/18/how-to-make-pvc-pipe-xylophone-instrument/
  - 👆 **Straw Flute:** http://krokotak.com/2013/04/singing-straws/
  - 👆 **Pringle's Can Drums:** https://www.thetaylor-house.com/upcycled-pringles-can-diy-drum/
  - 👆 **Homemade French Horn:** https://www.savvyhomemade.com/homemade-french-horn-for-kids/
  - 👆 **Popsicle Stick Harmonica:** http://www.housingaforest.com/popsicle-stick-harmonica/
  - 👆 **Cardboard Guitar:** http://www.minieco.co.uk/cardboard-instruments/

  Once the students have completed the project, have them take a picture and add it to their unit project sheet on SW pg. 34.

Projects for this Week

- ✂ **Coloring Pages** – Have the students color the following pages from *Physics for the Grammar Stage Coloring Pages*: Waves pg. 21.

✂ **Water Waves** – Have the students make waves in water. You will need a bowl of water and a small pebble. Have the students gently drop the pebble into the center of the bowl. Have them observe the resulting waves that are created.

✂ **String Waves** – Have the students do the "See for yourself" activity on pg. 203 of the *Usborne Science Encyclopedia*. You will need a string for this activity.

✂ **Sound Waves** – Have the students see how sound makes particles vibrate. You will need an oatmeal container with a plastic lid, a handful of sand, and a source of sound. Have the students place the sand on the top of the plastic lid of the oatmeal container. Then, turn on the music and observe what happens to the sand. (*You should see the sand begin to move and bounce around. If you don't, you may need to move the sound source closer to the container or turn up the volume.*)

Memorization

This week, continue working on memorizing the *Sound* Poem. (SW pg. 122)

Quiz

Weekly Quiz
"Sound Unit Week 2 Quiz" on SW pg. Q-16.

Quiz Answers
1. Waves carry energy.
2. True
3. B, A
4. Answers will vary

Possible Schedules for Week 2

Two Days a Week Schedule	
Day 1	**Day 2**
❏ Read the first page from the Waves spread (Watch the first half of the video) ❏ Add information about waves to the students' Narration Page ❏ Do the Scientific Demonstration: Twang ❏ Work on memorizing the *Sound* poem ❏ Define longitudinal waves and transverse waves	❏ Read the second page from the Waves spread (Watch the second half of the video) ❏ Add information about waves to the students' Narration Page ❏ Work on the Homemade Sound Project ❏ Give Sound Week 2 quiz

Five Days a Week Schedule				
Day 1	**Day 2**	**Day 3**	**Day 4**	**Day 5**
❏ Do the Scientific Demonstration: Twang ❏ Define longitudinal waves and transverse waves ❏ Choose one or more of the additional books to read from this week	❏ Read the first page from the Waves spread (Watch the first half of the video) ❏ Add information about waves to the students' Narration Page ❏ Complete the Water Waves Project	❏ Read the second page from the Waves spread (Watch the second half of the video) ❏ Add information about waves to the students' Narration Page ❏ Complete the String Waves Project	❏ Complete the Sound Waves Project ❏ Choose one or more of the additional books to read from this week	❏ Give Sound Week 2 quiz ❏ Work on the Homemade Sound Project
All Week Long				
❏ Work on memorizing the *Sound* poem				

Week 3: Wave Behavior Lesson Plans

Scientific Demonstration: Boom!

Supplies Needed
- ✓ Cup
- ✓ Rubber band

Purpose
This demonstration is meant to help the students hear the effect of solids on the speed of sound.

Instructions and Explanation
The instructions and explanation for this scientific demonstration are found on pp. 214-215 of *Janice VanCleave's Physics for Every Kid*. Have the students complete the Lab Report on SW pg. 41.

Take it Further
Have the students do another sound-related demonstration - "Spoon-bell" on pp. 230-231 of *Janice VanCleave's Physics for Every Kid*.

Science-Oriented Books

Reading Assignments
- 📖 *Usborne Science Encyclopedia pp. 204-205 Wave Behavior*
- 📖 *No pages are scheduled for younger students. Instead, have the students watch the following video to learn more about wave behavior:*
  - 🖱 https://www.youtube.com/watch?v=TfYCnOvNnFU

(Optional) Additional topics to explore this week: *DK Children's Encyclopedia pg. 127 (Hearing)*

Discussion Questions
After reading the selected pages, ask the following questions for your discussion time.

Wave Behavior
- **?** What are the three ways a wave can change?
- **?** What happens when a wave is reflected? Refracted? Diffracted?
- **?** What happens when two or more waves meet?
- **?** What is the difference between constructive and destructive interference?

(Optional) Additional Books
- 📖 *How Does Sound Change? (Light and Sound Waves Close-Up)* by Robin Johnson (Author)
- 📖 *How Sound Moves (Science Readers: Content and Literacy)* by Sharon Coan
- 📖 *Waves and Information Transfer (Catch a Wave)* by Heather C Hudak

Notebooking

Writing Assignments

☐ **Narration Page –** Have the students dictate, copy, or write three to five sentences on wave behavior on SW pg. 40.

☐ **(Optional) Lapbook –** Have the students complete the Wave Behavior Pocket Guide on pp. 22-23 of *Physics for the Grammar Stage Lapbooking Templates*. Have them cut out the pages for the pocket and the cards. Then, have the students color the pictures. If you are using the blank cards, have the students add a sentence about how waves are affected by reflection, refraction, interference, and diffraction on the respective cards. Finally, have the students glue the pocket into the lapbook and insert the cards.

Vocabulary

The following definition is a guide. The students' definition does not need to match word for word.

✏ **Interference –** The effect that occurs when two waves meet. (SW pg. 110)

Multi-week Projects and Activities

Unit Project

✂ **Homemade Sound –** This week, have the students continue to add to their suite of homemade instruments. Choose one of the projects from the list below that you have not already done:

✋ **PVC Pipe Xylophone:** https://frugalfun4boys.com/2015/03/18/how-to-make-pvc-pipe-xylophone-instrument/

✋ **Straw Flute:** http://krokotak.com/2013/04/singing-straws/

✋ **Pringle's Can Drums:** https://www.thetaylor-house.com/upcycled-pringles-can-diy-drum/

✋ **Homemade French Horn:** https://www.savvyhomemade.com/homemade-french-horn-for-kids/

✋ **Popsicle Stick Harmonica:** http://www.housingaforest.com/popsicle-stick-harmonica/

✋ **Cardboard Guitar:** http://www.minieco.co.uk/cardboard-instruments/

Once the students have completed the project, have them take a picture and add it to their unit project sheet on SW pg. 35.

Projects for this Week

✂ **Coloring Pages –** Have the students color the following pages from *Physics for the Grammar Stage Coloring Pages*: Interference pg. 22.

✂ **Giant Wave –** Make a giant wave for your students to play with. You will need string, popsicle sticks, ruler, pencil, and a hot glue gun. The directions for this project can be found here:

✋ http://blog.teachersource.com/2015/01/13/making-waves/

✂ **Interference –** Have the students do the "See for yourself" activity on pg. 205 of the

Usborne Science Encyclopedia. You will need two small pebbles and a bathtub full of water.

Memorization

🗣 This week, begin working on memorizing the *Sound* Poem. (SW pg. 122)

Quiz

Weekly Quiz

✦ "Sound Unit Week 3 Quiz" on SW pg. Q-17.

Quiz Answers

1. False (*A wave can change speed, direction, or shape when it passes into a different medium.*)
2. Interference
3. B, A
4. Answers will vary

Possible Schedules for Week 3

Two Days a Week Schedule	
Day 1	**Day 2**
❑ Read the first page from the Wave Behavior spread (Watch the first half of the video) ❑ Add information about wave behavior to the students' Narration Page ❑ Do the Scientific Demonstration: Boom! ❑ Work on memorizing the *Sound* poem ❑ Define interference	❑ Read the second page from the Wave Behavior spread (Watch the second half of the video) ❑ Add information about wave behavior to the students' Narration Page ❑ Work on the Homemade Sound Project ❑ Give Sound Week 3 quiz

Five Days a Week Schedule				
Day 1	**Day 2**	**Day 3**	**Day 4**	**Day 5**
❑ Do the Scientific Demonstration: Boom! ❑ Choose one or more of the additional books to read from this week	❑ Read the first page from the Wave Behavior spread (Watch the first half of the video) ❑ Add information about wave behavior to the students' Narration Page ❑ Define interference	❑ Read the second page from the Wave Behavior spread (Watch the second half of the video) ❑ Add information about wave behavior to the students' Narration Page ❑ Complete the Interference Project	❑ Complete the Giant Wave Project ❑ Choose one or more of the additional books to read from this week	❑ Give Sound Week 3 quiz ❑ Work on the Homemade Sound Project
All Week Long				
❑ Work on memorizing the *Sound* poem				

Week 4: Musical Instruments Lesson Plans

Scientific Demonstration: Straw Flute

Supplies Needed
- ✓ Straw
- ✓ Scissors
- ✓ Ruler
- ✓ Marking pen

Purpose
This demonstration is meant to help the students see how the length of a flute affects the sound it makes.

Instructions and Explanation
The instructions and explanation for this scientific demonstration are found on pp. 224-225 of *Janice VanCleave's Physics for Every Kid*. Have the students complete the Lab Report on SW pg. 43.

Take it Further
Have the students do another sound-related demonstration - "String Music" on pp. 220-221 of *Janice VanCleave's Physics for Every Kid*.

Science-Oriented Books

Reading Assignments
- 📖 *Usborne Science Encyclopedia pp. 208-209 Musical Instruments*
- 📖 *Usborne Children's Encyclopedia pg. 209 Sound, DK Children's Encyclopedia pp. 176-177 Music*

(Optional) Additional topics to explore this week: *DK Children's Encyclopedia pg. 127 (Hearing)*

Discussion Questions
After reading the selected pages, ask the following questions for your discussion time.

Musical Instruments
- **?** How do stringed instruments work?
- **?** How do wind instruments work?
- **?** How do percussion instruments work?
- **?** How do electric instruments work?
- **?** What is pitch?

(Optional) Additional Books
- 📖 *The Science of Music (Super-Awesome Science)* by Cecilia Pinto McCarthy
- 📖 *Science of Music: Discovering Sound (Science in Action)* by Karen Latchana Kenney

📖 *Musical Instruments (How Things Work)* by Ade Deane-pratt

Notebooking

Writing Assignments

☐ **Narration Page** – Have the students dictate, copy, or write three to five sentences on musical instruments on SW pg. 42.

☐ **(Optional) Lapbook** – Have the students complete the How Instruments Work Tab-book on pg. 24 of *Physics for the Grammar Stage Lapbooking Templates*. Have them cut out the pages for the tab-book and color the pictures. Then, have the students add a sentence about how stringed instruments work on the string page, how wind instruments work on the wind page, and how percussion instruments work on the percussion page. Assemble the tab-book and staple it together on the dashed lines. Finally, have the students glue the mini-book into the lapbook.

Vocabulary

The following definition is a guide. The students' definition does not need to match word for word.

✏ **Resonate** – To vibrate at the same frequency as something else. (SW pg. 115)

Multi-week Projects and Activities

Unit Project

✂ **Homemade Sound** – This week, have the students continue to add to their suite of homemade instruments. Choose one of the projects from the list below that you have not already done:

- 🖐 **PVC Pipe Xylophone:** https://frugalfun4boys.com/2015/03/18/how-to-make-pvc-pipe-xylophone-instrument/
- 🖐 **Straw Flute:** http://krokotak.com/2013/04/singing-straws/
- 🖐 **Pringle's Can Drums:** https://www.thetaylor-house.com/upcycled-pringles-can-diy-drum/
- 🖐 **Homemade French Horn:** https://www.savvyhomemade.com/homemade-french-horn-for-kids/
- 🖐 **Popsicle Stick Harmonica:** http://www.housingaforest.com/popsicle-stick-harmonica/
- 🖐 **Cardboard Guitar:** http://www.minieco.co.uk/cardboard-instruments/

Once the students have completed the project, have them take a picture and add it to their unit project sheet on SW pg. 35.

Projects for this Week

✂ **Coloring Pages** – Have the students color the following pages from *Physics for the Grammar Stage Coloring Pages*: Instruments pg 23.

✂ **Physics of Music** – Have the students listen to some classical music. You can find directions for this activity here:

      ⌐ https://elementalscience.com/blogs/science-activities/physics-of-music

✂ **Bottle Instrument –** Have the students do the "See for yourself" activity on pg. 209 of the *Usborne Science Encyclopedia.* You will need an empty bottle and some water for this activity.

Memorization

🗣 This week, continue working on memorizing the *Sound* Poem. (SW pg. 122)

Quiz

Weekly Quiz

     ✦ "Sound Unit Week 4 Quiz" on SW pg. Q-18.

Quiz Answers

1. A, C, B
2. True
3. Answers will vary

Possible Schedules for Week 4

Two Days a Week Schedule	
Day 1	**Day 2**
❑ Read the first page from the Musical Instruments spread (Sound from the Usborne book) ❑ Add information about musical instruments to the students' Narration Page ❑ Do the Scientific Demonstration: Straw Flute ❑ Work on memorizing the *Sound* poem ❑ Define resonate	❑ Read the first page from the Musical Instruments spread (Music from the DK book) ❑ Add information about musical instruments to the students' Narration Page ❑ Work on the Homemade Sound Project ❑ Give Sound Week 4 quiz

Five Days a Week Schedule				
Day 1	**Day 2**	**Day 3**	**Day 4**	**Day 5**
❑ Do the Scientific Demonstration: Straw Flute ❑ Define resonate ❑ Choose one or more of the additional books to read from this week	❑ Read the first page from the Musical Instruments spread (Sound from the Usborne book) ❑ Add information about musical instruments to the students' Narration Page ❑ Complete the Physics of Music Project	❑ Read the first page from the Musical Instruments spread (Music from the DK book) ❑ Add information about musical instruments to the students' Narration Page ❑ Complete the Bottle Instrument Project	❑ Work on the Homemade Sound Project ❑ Choose one or more of the additional books to read from this week	❑ Give Sound Week 4 quiz
All Week Long				
❑ Work on memorizing the *Sound* poem				

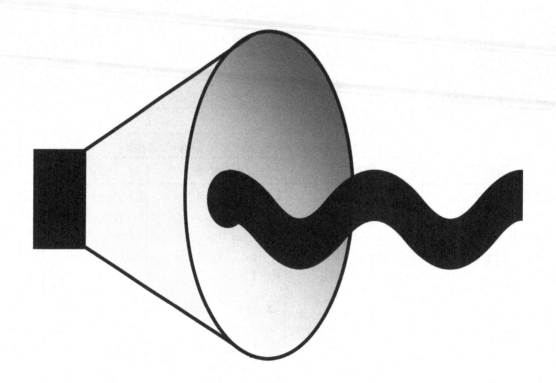

Physics for the Grammar Stage

Electricity Unit

Electricity Unit Overview
(5 weeks)

Books Scheduled
Required Encyclopedia
📖 *Usborne Science Encyclopedia*

OR

📖 *Usborne Children's Encyclopedia* and *DK Children's Encyclopedia*

Optional Additional Encyclopedia
📖 *Basher Science Physics: Why Matter Matters!*

Scientific Demonstrations Book
📖 *JVC Physics for Every Kid*

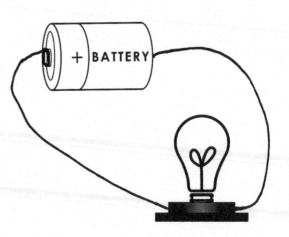

Sequence for Study
✎ **Week 1:** Electricity
✎ **Week 2:** Circuits and Batteries
✎ **Week 3:** Magnets
✎ **Week 4:** Electronics
✎ **Week 5:** Computers and Coding

Electricity Unit Memory Work
Electricity
Electricity is charges that move
Particles flowing give power to groove

Conductors allow the current to flow
Insulators stop current, no more go

Circuits show the path of the particles
Wires are the quick shipping articles

Around in a circle, the currents flow
Resistors will cause the currents to slow

Capacitors store and release power
Electronics use to do tasks each hour

Computers store and use information
Binary code is the bit foundation

Supplies Needed for the Unit

Week	Supplies needed
1	Comb, Tissue Paper, Scissors, Ruler
2	Clothespin, D-battery, Foil, Flashlight bulb, Tape, Testing materials (e.g., rubber band, paper coins, paper clip, ruler)
3	Straight pin, Thread, Tissue paper, Bar magnet, Scissors
4	Old Electronic, Screwdriver, Newspaper
5	Computer, Access to the Internet
Unit Project	Snap Circuits Jr. SC-100 Electronics Discovery Kit or a comparable circuit kit

Unit Vocabulary

1. **Conductor** – A substance through which current can flow.
2. **Electricity** – The effect caused by the presence or movement of electrically charged particles.
3. **Insulator** – A substance through which current cannot flow.
4. **Battery** – A source of stored electrical energy.
5. **Circuit** – The path along which electrical current flows.
6. **Magnet** – An object that attracts iron, steel, and metals.
7. **Pole** – One of the two points on a magnet where the force of attraction or repulsion is strongest.
8. **Capacitor** – A device that stores electrical energy until it is needed.
9. **Resistor** – An electrical component that reduces the flow of current.
10. **Binary Code** – A way of representing information using only 1's and 0's.

Week 1: Electricity Lesson Plans

Scientific Demonstration: Streamers

Supplies Needed
- ✓ Comb
- ✓ Tissue Paper
- ✓ Scissors
- ✓ Ruler

Purpose
This demonstration is meant to help the students see static electricity.

Instructions and Explanation
The instructions and explanation for this scientific demonstration are found on pp. 18-19 of *Janice VanCleave's Physics for Every Kid*. Have the students complete the Lab Report on SW pg. 49.

Take it Further
Have the students do another electricity-related demonstration - "Move Away" on pp. 20-21 of *Janice VanCleave's Physics for Every Kid*.

Science-Oriented Books

Reading Assignments
- *Usborne Science Encyclopedia pp. 228-229 Electricity*
- *Usborne Children's Encyclopedia pp. 210-211 Electricity, DK Children's Encyclopedia pg. 87 Electricity*

(Optional) Additional topics to explore this week: *Basher Physics pg. 112 Static Electricity*

Discussion Questions
After reading the selected pages, ask the following questions for your discussion time.

Electricity
- **?** What is electricity?
- **?** What is electric current?
- **?** What is a conductor? An insulator?
- **?** What is static electricity?
- **?** What causes lightning?

(Optional) Additional Books
- *The Magic School Bus And The Electric Field Trip* by Joanna Cole and Bruce Degan
- *Switch On, Switch Off (Let's-Read-and-Find-Out Science 2)* by Melvin Berger
- *Electricity (Science Readers: Content and Literacy)* by Hugh Westrup
- *You Wouldn't Want to Live Without Electricity* by Ian Graham and Rory Walker

Notebooking

Writing Assignments

- ☐ **Narration Page –** Have the students dictate, copy, or write three to five sentences about electricity on SW pg. 48. For example, this week the students could dictate, copy, or write the following:

    Electricity is a useful form of energy used to power device. It is the effect created as charged particles move. Electric current is the flow of the charged particles. Conductors allow electric current to flow through them, while insulators do not. Static electricity is electricity that is held by a material. Lightning is caused by static electricity that builds up in a storm cloud.

- ☐ **(Optional) Lapbook –** Have the students complete the Electricity Mini-book on pg. 27 of *Physics for the Grammar Stage Lapbooking Templates*. Have them cut out the mini-book template and color the picture on the front. Then, have the students add a sentence or two about electricity. Then, have the students glue the sheet into the lapbook. Have them fold the mini-book and glue it into the lapbook.

- ☐ **(Optional) Lapbook –** Have the students complete the Conductor vs. Insulator Tab-book on pg. 28 of *Physics for the Grammar Stage Lapbooking Templates*. Have them cut out the pages for the tab-book and color the pictures. Then, have the students add a sentence about conductors on the respective page and a sentence about insulators on the respective page. Assemble the tab-book and staple it together on the dashed lines. Finally, have the students glue the mini-book into the lapbook.

Vocabulary

The following definitions are a guide. The students' definitions do not need to match word for word.

- 🏷 **Conductor –** A substance through which current can flow. (SW pg. 106)
- 🏷 **Electricity –** The effect caused by the presence or movement of electrically charged particles. (SW pg. 107)
- 🏷 **Insulator –** A substance through which current cannot flow. (SW pg. 110)

Multi-week Projects and Activities

Unit Project

- ✂ **Circuit Testing –** For this project, you will need a Snap Circuits Jr. SC-100 Electronics Discovery Kit or a comparable circuit kit that contains the materials for at least 10 projects relating to electricity, circuits, batteries, and machines. You can purchase the Snap Circuits kit at Rainbow Resources, CBD, Home Science Tools, or Amazon. Each week, your students will choose one or two projects to complete. After they are done, take a picture of what they created and add the photo, along with a sentence or two of what they learned, to the Circuit Testing Diary in the SW on pp. 46. This week, we recommend trying Project #1 - Electric Light & Switch or #9 - Conduction Detector.

Projects for this Week

✂ **Coloring Pages –** Have the students color the following pages from *Physics for the Grammar Stage Coloring Pages*: Conductors and Insulators pg. 24.

✂ **Electric Bulb –** Have the students make a light bulb glow without being plugged in! You will need a balloon and a compact fluorescent light bulb. Blow up the balloon and then have the students rub it back and forth on the top of their heads for about twenty seconds. Quickly move the balloon close to the light bulb and watch what happens! (*The light bulb should begin to glow. Rubbing the balloon on their heads caused a buildup of electrons on the surface of the balloon. As soon as the electrons get near the light bulb, the vapor in the tubes is charged, causing it to become excited and give off visible light.*)

✂ **Static Electricity –** Have the students do the "See for yourself" activity on pg. 228 of the *Usborne Science Encyclopedia*. You will need thread, tape, two balloons, and a sweater or scarf for this activity.

✂ **Indoor Lightning –** Have the students make lightning in the kitchen. You will need a pencil with an eraser, an aluminum tray or pie tin, wool cloth, a styrofoam plate or meat tray, and a thumbtack. Get directions for this project at Learn, Play, Imagine:
🖱 http://www.learnplayimagine.com/2013/04/how-to-make-lightning.html

Memorization

🗣 This week, begin working on memorizing the *Electricity* poem. (SW pg. 123)

Quiz

Weekly Quiz

🗝 "Electricity Unit Week 1 Quiz" on SW pg. Q-19.

Quiz Answers

1. True
2. Conductors allow electric current to flow through them, while insulators do not.
3. Static electricity
4. Answers will vary

Possible Schedules for Week 1

Two Days a Week Schedule

Day 1	Day 2
❏ Read the second page from the Electricity spread (Electricity)	❏ Read the second page from the Electricity spread (Electricty)
❏ Add information about electricity to the students' Narration Page	❏ Add information about electricity to the students' Narration Page
❏ Do the Scientific Demonstration: Streamer	❏ Define conductor and insulator
❏ Work on memorizing the *Electricity* poem	❏ Work on the Circuit Testing Project
❏ Define electricity	❏ Give Energy Week 1 quiz

Five Days a Week Schedule

Day 1	Day 2	Day 3	Day 4	Day 5
❏ Do the Scientific Demonstration: Bonk! ❏ Define energy ❏ Choose one or more of the additional books to read from this week	❏ Read the second page from the Electricity spread (Electricity) ❏ Add information about electricity to the students' Narration Page ❏ Complete the Electric Bulb Race Project	❏ Read the second page from the Electricity spread (Electricity) ❏ Add information about electricity to the students' Narration Page ❏ Complete the Static Electricity Project	❏ Complete the Indoor Lightning Project ❏ Define conductor, electricity, and insulator	❏ Give Electricity Week 1 quiz ❏ Work on the Circuit Testing Project

All Week Long

❏ Work on memorizing the *Electricity* poem

Week 2: Circuits and Batteries Lesson Plans

Scientific Demonstration: Conductor

Supplies Needed
- ✓ Clothespin
- ✓ D-battery
- ✓ Foil
- ✓ Flashlight bulb
- ✓ Tape
- ✓ Testing materials (e.g., rubber band, paper coins, paper clip, ruler)

Purpose

This demonstration is meant for students to build their own circuit and use it to determine which materials conduct electricity.

Instructions and Explanation

The instructions and explanation for this scientific demonstration are found on pp. 10-11 of *Janice VanCleave's Physics for Every Kid*. Have the students complete the Lab Report on SW pg. 51.

Take it Further

Have the students do another electricity-related demonstration - "Hot" on pp. 12-13 of *Janice VanCleave's Physics for Every Kid*.

Science-Oriented Books

Reading Assignments
- 📖 *Usborne Science Encyclopedia pp. 230–231 Electricity, part 2*
- 📖 *DK Children's Encyclopedia pg. 59 Circuits; you can also watch the following video about batteries:*
    - 🖱 https://www.youtube.com/watch?v=RWWLfUIiMAw

(Optional) Additional topics to explore this week: *Basher Physics pg. 114 Electric Current*

Discussion Questions

After reading the selected pages, ask the following questions for your discussion time.

Circuits and Batteries
- ❓ What is an electric circuit?
- ❓ What is the difference between a series circuit and a parallel circuit?
- ❓ How does electricity work at home?
- ❓ What is a battery?
- ❓ How does a solar cell work?

(Optional) Additional Books
- 📖 *Circuits (Science Readers: Content and Literacy)* by Theodore Buchanan
- 📖 *Making a Circuit (It's Electric!)* by Chris Oxlade
- 📖 *How Batteries Work (Connect with Electricity)* by Victoria G. Christensen
- 📖 *How Does a Battery Work? (Electrified!)* by Roman Wilson

Notebooking

Writing Assignments
- ☐ **Narration Page –** Have the students dictate, copy, or write three to five sentences on circuits and batteries on SW pg. 51.
- ☐ **(Optional) Lapbook –** Have the students complete the Circuit Wheel-book on pg. 29 of *Physics for the Grammar Stage Lapbooking Templates.* Have them cut out the wheel templates. On one third of the wheel with the battery picture have the students label the battery with "energy source." On one third of the wheel with the wires picture have the students label the wires with "pathway." On one third of the wheel with the light bulb picture have the students label the light bulb with "component." Then, use a brad to attach the two pages together so that the cover spins to reveal one part at a time. Finally, have them glue the mini-book into the lapbook.

Vocabulary
The following definitions are a guide. The students' definitions do not need to match word for word.
- 🖊 **Battery –** A source of stored electrical energy. (SW pg. 104)
- 🖊 **Circuit –** The path along which electrical current flows. (SW pg. 105)

Multi-week Projects and Activities

Unit Project
- ✂ **Circuit Testing –** Have the students build and test one or two more projects from the Snap Circuits Jr. SC-100 Electronics Discovery Kit. After they are done, take a picture of what they created and add the photo, along with a sentence or two of what they learned, to the Circuit Testing Diary in the SW on pp. 46. This week, we recommend trying Project #5 - Lamp & Fan in Series and Project #6 - Lamp & Fan in Parallel or Project #47 - This or That.

Projects for this Week
- ✂ **Coloring Pages –** Have the students color the following pages from *Physics for the Grammar Stage Coloring Pages*: Circuit pg. 25, Battery pg. 26.
- ✂ **Simple Circuit –** Have the students build a simple circuit with just a watch battery, some cardboard, tape, and an LED light bulb. Have the students cut out two of the same shape from the cardboard. Cut a slit on one of the shapes large enough to fit the LED bulb. Flip the shape over and insert the light bulb through the slit. Then place the battery

in between the wires so that the light bulb turns on. Use the tape to secure the battery in place and to ensure that the back wire stays firmly in place. Next, use another piece of tape to keep the other wire just above the battery. Cover the simple circuit with the other cardboard shape and write "Press Here" on the spot that will push the wire down to connect with the battery and light up the bulb!

✂ **Simple Battery –** Have the students do the "See for yourself" activity on pg. 231 of the *Usborne Science Encyclopedia*. You will need foil, a paper towel, water, salt, and 12 pennies for this activity.

✂ **Steady Hand Circuit –** Have the students play a game of Operation, which requires a steady hand to not complete the circuit and make noise. If you don't own this game, you can make your own steady hand circuit using the directions found here:

🖱 http://www.123homeschool4me.com/2016/06/electronics-project-for-kids-steady.html

Memorization

🗣 This week, continue working on memorizing the *Electricity* poem. (SW pg. 123)

Quiz

Weekly Quiz

⚡ "Electricity Unit Week 2 Quiz" on SW pg. Q-20.

Quiz Answers

1. The path of electrical current.
2. Parallel circuit - A circuit where there is more than one path for the electric current to travel. Series circuit - A circuit where the components are one after the other.
3. Chemical, electrical
4. Answers will vary

Possible Schedules for Week 2

Two Days a Week Schedule	
Day 1	**Day 2**
❑ Read the first page from the Electricity, part 2 spread (Circuits) ❑ Add information about circuits and batteries to the students' Narration Page ❑ Do the Scientific Demonstration: Wind Energy ❑ Work on memorizing the *Electricity* poem	❑ Read the second page from the Electricity, part 2 spread (Watch the battery video) ❑ Add information about circuits and batteries to the students' Narration Page ❑ Work on the Circuit Testing Project ❑ Define battery and circuit ❑ Give Electricity Week 2 quiz

Five Days a Week Schedule				
Day 1	**Day 2**	**Day 3**	**Day 4**	**Day 5**
❑ Do the Scientific Demonstration: Wind Energy ❑ Define battery and circuit	❑ Read the first page from the Electricity, part 2 spread (Circuits) ❑ Add information about circuits and batteries to the students' Narration Page ❑ Complete the Simple Circuit Project	❑ Read the second page from the Electricity, part 2 spread (Watch the battery video) ❑ Add information about circuits and batteries to the students' Narration Page ❑ Complete the Simple Battery Project	❑ Complete the Steady Hand Circuit Project ❑ Choose one or more of the additional books to read from this week	❑ Give Electricity Week 2 quiz ❑ Work on the Circuit Testing Project
All Week Long				
❑ Work on memorizing the *Electricity* poem				

Week 3: Magnets Lesson Plans

Scientific Demonstration: Suspended Airplane

Supplies Needed
- ✓ Straight pin
- ✓ Thread
- ✓ Tissue paper
- ✓ Bar magnet
- ✓ Scissors

Purpose
This demonstration is meant to use magnetic force.

Instructions and Explanation
The instructions and explanation for this scientific demonstration are found on pp. 40-41 of *Janice VanCleave's Physics for Every Kid*. Have the students complete the Lab Report on SW pg. 53.

Take it Further
Have the students do another magnet-related demonstration - "Magnetic Strength" on pp. 42-43 of *Janice VanCleave's Physics for Every Kid*.

Science-Oriented Books

Reading Assignments
- 📖 *Usborne Science Encyclopedia pp. 232-233 Magnetism*
- 📖 *Usborne Children's Encyclopedia pp. 204-205 Magnets, DK Children's Encyclopedia pg. 151 Magnets*

(Optional) Additional topics to explore this week: *Basher Physics pg. 116 Magnetism, USE pp. 234-235 Magnetism, part 2*

Discussion Questions
After reading the selected pages, ask the following questions for your discussion time.

Magnetism
- **?** What is magnetism?
- **?** Which poles attract?
- **?** Which poles repel?
- **?** What is a magnetic field?
- **?** How does electromagnetism work?

(Optional) Additional Books
- 📖 *What Makes a Magnet? (Let's-Read-and-Find-Out Science 2)* by Franklyn M. Branley and True Kelley
- 📖 *Magnets: Pulling Together, Pushing Apart (Amazing Science)* by Natalie M. Rosinsky

📖 *What Magnets Can Do (Rookie Read-About Science)* by Allan Fowler

📖 *A Look at Magnets (Science Builders)* by Barbara Alpert

Notebooking

Writing Assignments

☐ **Narration Page –** Have the students dictate, copy, or write three to five sentences on magnets on SW pg. 52.

☐ **(Optional) Lapbook –** Have the students complete the Magnet Sheet on pg. 30 of *Physics for the Grammar Stage Lapbooking Templates*. Have them cut out the sheet and color the picture. Then, have the students add a sentence or two about magnets and how they work under the heading on the sheet. Finally, have the students glue the sheet into the lapbook.

Vocabulary

The following definitions are a guide. The students' definitions do not need to match word for word.

↻ **Magnet –** An object that attracts iron, steel, and metals. (SW pg. 111)

↻ **Pole –** One of the two points on a magnet where the force of attraction or repulsion is strongest. (SW pg. 113)

Multi-week Projects and Activities

Unit Project

✂ **Circuit Testing –** Have the students build and test one or two more projects from the Snap Circuits Jr. SC-100 Electronics Discovery Kit. After they are done, take a picture of what they created and add the photo, along with a sentence or two of what they learned, to the Circuit Testing Diary in the SW on pp. 46. This week, we recommend trying Project #2 - DC Motor & Switch or Project #19 - Space War.

Projects for this Week

✂ **Coloring Pages –** Have the students color the following pages from *Physics for the Grammar Stage Coloring Pages*: Magnets pg. 27.

✂ **Magnetic Exploration –** Have the students observe and learn about magnets. You can do this by giving the students several types of magnets (bar magnets, horseshoe magnets, or neodymium magnets) and several types of objects (marbles, paper clips, paper, pins, plastic spoons, and more.) Allow the students to play with the magnets and the objects. Let them see how they are attracted to each other or how they repel each other. Let them observe what objects can be picked up by the magnets and which ones cannot.

✂ **Magnetic Field –** Have the students do the "See for yourself" activity on pg. 233 of the *Usborne Science Encyclopedia*. You will need iron filings, sheet of paper, and a magnet.

✂ **Magnet Train –** Have the students create a small train using neodymium magnets, a battery, and a roll of thin copper wire. You can get the directions for this project from

Frugal Fun 4 Boys:

🖱 https://frugalfun4boys.com/2015/03/10/how-to-build-a-simple-electromagnetic-train/

Memorization

This week, continue working on memorizing the *Electricity* poem. (SW pg. 123)

Quiz

Weekly Quiz

↯ "Electricity Unit Week 3 Quiz" on SW pg. Q-21.

Quiz Answers

1. False (*For magnets, like poles repel each other, while unlike poles attract.*)
2. Attract, repel
3. Magnetic field
4. Answers will vary

Possible Schedules for Week 3

Two Days a Week Schedule	
Day 1	**Day 2**
❑ Read the first page from the Magnetism spread (Magnets) ❑ Add information about magnets to the students' Narration Page ❑ Do the Scientific Demonstration: Suspended Airplane ❑ Define magnet and pole	❑ Read the second page from the Magnetism spread (Magnets) ❑ Add information about magnets to the students' Narration Page ❑ Work on memorizing the *Electricity* poem ❑ Work on the Circuit Testing Project ❑ Give Electricity Week 3 quiz

Five Days a Week Schedule				
Day 1	**Day 2**	**Day 3**	**Day 4**	**Day 5**
❑ Do the Scientific Demonstration: Suspended Airplane ❑ Define magnet and pole	❑ Read the first page from the Magnetism spread (Magnets) ❑ Add information about magnets to the students' Narration Page ❑ Complete the Magnet Exploration Project	❑ Read the second page from the Magnetism spread (Magnets) ❑ Add information about magnets to the students' Narration Page ❑ Complete the Magnetic Field Project	❑ Complete the Magnet Train Project ❑ Choose one or more of the additional books to read from this week	❑ Give Electricity Week 3 quiz ❑ Work on the Circuit Testing Project
All Week Long				
❑ Work on memorizing the *Electricity* poem				

Week 4: Electronics Lesson Plans

Scientific Demonstration: Deconstruction

Supplies Needed
- ✓ Old Electronic
- ✓ Screwdriver
- ✓ Newspaper

Purpose
This demonstration is meant to give students a chance to practice reverse engineering to see what is inside an electronic. (**Note**—*This demonstration is best to do after the reading, as the students will have a better understanding of the different components.*)

Instructions
1. Begin by laying out the newspaper over a table.
2. Then, use the screwdriver to help the students open up the old electronic so that you can see the circuit boards inside.
3. Let the students observe the insides of the electronic. Have them look for the different components – capacitors, diodes, transistors, and resistors.
4. As they observe, let them remove any parts to dig deeper into the electronic.
5. Have the students write what they learn on the Lab Report on SW pg. 55.

Take it Further
Have the students reverse engineer another type of electronic and see how the components compare – are they the same or different?

Alternative Demonstration
If you do not have access to an electronic that your students can reverse engineer, do the following demonstration instead - "Galvanometer" on pp. 14-15 of *Janice VanCleave's Physics for Every Kid.*

Science-Oriented Books

Reading Assignments
- 📖 *Usborne Science Encyclopedia pp. 236-237 (Electronics)*
- 📖 *No pages scheduled for younger students. Instead, have the students follow along with the older students reading assignment. You may need to summarize the different sections for them.*

  (Optional) Additional topics to explore this week: *USE pp. 238-239 Digital Electronics*

Discussion Questions
After reading the selected pages, ask the following questions for your discussion time.

Electronics
? What is an electronic?

? What is a resistor?

? How do we tell how much resistance a resistor gives?

? What is a diode?

? What is a transistor?

? What is a capacitor?

(Optional) Additional Books

📖 *Encyclopedia of Electronic Components Volume 1: Resistors, Capacitors, Inductors, Switches, Encoders, Relays, Transistors* by Charles Platt

Notebooking

Writing Assignments

☐ **Narration Page** – Have the students dictate, copy, or write three to five sentences on electronics on SW pg. 54.

☐ **(Optional) Lapbook** – Have the students complete the Electronics Fold-out book on pg. 31 of *Physics for the Grammar Stage Lapbooking Templates*. Have them cut out the template and the mini-book cover. Have the students color the pictures. Then, have the students write the definition of the components (capacitor, diode, resistor, and transistor) on their respective pages. The definitions for capacitor and resistor are in the vocabulary section below. Here are the definitions for diode and transistor for your reference:

✏ **Diode** – An electrical component that is used as an electrical switch.

✏ **Transistor** – An electrical component that allows the current to flow through in only one direction.

Next, have the students draw a line from the capacitor and resistor component squares to where the parts are in the circuit on the middle. A labeled circuit has been provided here for your reference. Finally, have them fold down the flaps, glue on the cover, and add the mini-book into the lapbook.

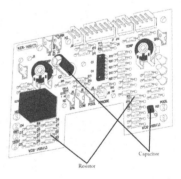

Vocabulary

The following definitions are a guide. The students' definitions do not need to match word for word.

✏ **Capacitor** – A device that stores electrical energy until it is needed. (SW pg. 105)

✏ **Resistor** – An electrical component that reduces the flow of current . (SW pg. 114)

Multi-week Projects and Activities

Unit Project

✂ **Circuit Testing** – Have the students build and test one or two more projects from the

Snap Circuits Jr. SC-100 Electronics Discovery Kit. After they are done, take a picture of what they created and add the photo, along with a sentence or two of what they learned, to the Circuit Testing Diary in the SW on pp. 47. This week, we recommend trying Project #7 - Light Emitting Diode or Project #18 - Laser Gun.

Projects for this Week

✂ **Coloring Pages –** Have the students color the following pages from *Physics for the Grammar Stage Coloring Pages*: Electronics pg. 28.

✂ **Electronics Kit –** Have the students build a few electronics of their own. You can use the Snap Circuits kit from the unit project or you can purchase an electronics kit that requires soldering, if you think your students are up to the challenge. We recommend the following kits:
  ✓ Elenco AmeriKit Learn to Solder Kit
  ✓ Elenco FM Radio Kit

✂ **Resistors –** Have the students do the "See for yourself" activity on pg. 236 of the *Usborne Science Encyclopedia*. You can also identify one of the resistors you discovered in the demonstration.

Memorization

🗣 This week, continue working on memorizing the *Electricity* poem. (SW pg. 123)

Quiz

Weekly Quiz
♪ "Electricity Unit Week 4 Quiz" on SW pg. Q-22.

Quiz Answers
1. B,D,A,C
2. Electronic, current, task
3. Answers will vary

Possible Schedules for Week 4

Two Days a Week Schedule	
Day 1	**Day 2**
❑ Read the full spread from the Electronics spread ❑ Add information about electronics to the students' Narration Page ❑ Do the Scientific Demonstration: Hot Band ❑ Define capacitor and resistor	❑ Do the Scientific Demonstration: Deconstruction ❑ Work on memorizing the *Electricity* poem ❑ Work on the Circuit Testing Project ❑ Give Electricity Week 4 quiz

Five Days a Week Schedule				
Day 1	**Day 2**	**Day 3**	**Day 4**	**Day 5**
❑ Read the first page from the Electronics spread ❑ Add information about electronics to the students' Narration Page ❑ Complete the Resistor Project	❑ Read the second page from the Electronics spread ❑ Add information about electronics to the students' Narration Page ❑ Define capacitor and resistor	❑ Do the Scientific Demonstration: Deconstruction ❑ Choose one or more of the additional books to read from this week	❑ Complete the Electronics Kit Project ❑ Choose one or more of the additional books to read from this week	❑ Give Electricity Week 4 quiz ❑ Work on the Circuit Testing Project
All Week Long				
❑ Work on memorizing the *Electricity* poem				

Week 5: Computers and Coding Lesson Plans

Scientific Demonstration: Coding Basics

Supplies Needed
- ✓ Computer
- ✓ Access to the Internet

Purpose
This demonstration is meant to show the students practice coding.

Instructions and Explanation
Go to the following website and follow the prompts given:
- 🖱 http://www.crunchzilla.com/code-monster

(Note—*There is no lab report for this week.*)

Take it Further
Have the students take a simple coding course. You can find several ones for free from the following places:
- 🖱 https://code.org/student/elementary
- 🖱 https://www.codecademy.com/
- 🖱 https://www.khanacademy.org/computing/computer-programming

Science-Oriented Books

Reading Assignments
- 📖 *Usborne Science Encyclopedia pp. 240-241 Computers*
- 📖 *Usborne Children's Encyclopedia pp. 226-227 Computers, DK Children's Encyclopedia pg. 65 Coding, pg. 71 Computers*

(Optional) Additional topics to explore this week: *Basher Physics pg. 122 Semiconductors*

Discussion Questions
After reading the selected pages, ask the following questions for your discussion time.

Computers
- **?** What are computers?
- **?** What is the difference between computer hardware and software?
- **?** What is binary code?
- **?** What is a CPU?
- **?** How do computers store information?

(Optional) Additional Books
- 📖 *Grace Hopper: Queen of Computer Code (People Who Shaped Our World)* by Laurie Wallmark and Katy Wu
- 📖 *How to Code: A Step-By-Step Guide to Computer Coding* by Max Wainewright

📖 *Who Says Women Can't Be Computer Programmers?: The Story of Ada Lovelace* by Tanya Lee Stone and Marjorie Priceman

Notebooking

Writing Assignments

- ☐ **Narration Page –** Have the students dictate, copy, or write three to five sentences on computers and coding on SW pg. 56.
- ☐ **(Optional) Lapbook –** Have the students complete the Computer Mini-book on pp. 32 of *Physics for the Grammar Stage Lapbooking Templates*. Have them cut out the template for the mini-book and color the picture on the cover. Then, have the students write the a sentence or two with what they have learned about computers. Once they are done, glue the mini-book into the lapbook.
- ☐ **(Optional) Lapbook –** Have the students finish the Electricity lapbook. Have them cut out and color the cover on pg. 26 of *Physics for the Grammar Stage Lapbooking Templates*. Once they are done, have them glue the sheet on the front of the lapbook.

Vocabulary

The following definition is a guide. The students' definition does not need to match word for word.

- ✎ **Binary Code –** A way of representing information using only 1's and 0's. (SW pg. 104)

Multi-week Projects and Activities

Unit Project

- ✂ **Circuit Testing –** Have the students build and test one or two more projects from the Snap Circuits Jr. SC-100 Electronics Discovery Kit. After they are done, take a picture of what they created and add the photo, along with a sentence or two of what they learned, to the Circuit Testing Diary in the SW on pp. 47. This week, we recommend trying Project #40 - Motor-Controlled Sounds or Project #86 - Music Alarm Combo.

Projects for this Week

- ✂ **Coloring Pages –** Have the students color the following pages from *Physics for the Grammar Stage Coloring Pages*: Computer pg. 29.
- ✂ **Secret Code –** Have the students make up a secret code. Their code can use letters, numbers, or pictures to represent the letters of the alphabet. Have the students begin by creating a decoding sheet with the letters of the alphabet with the corresponding letter or symbol from their secret code. Then, have them write out several messages for you to decode. Once you decode their messages, you can send them one back using their secret code.
- ✂ **Binary Bracelet –** Have the students make a bracelet of their name in binary code. You will need two colors of beads and elastic jewelry cord. Directions for this project can be found here:

🖱 https://www.mamasmiles.com/stem-fun-for-kids/
✂ **LEGO Coding –** Have the students practicing coding with a free on-line game from LEGO, which can be found here:
  🖱 https://www.lego.com/en-us/campaigns/bits-and-bricks

Memorization

🗣 This week, continue working on memorizing the *Electricity* poem. (SW pg. 123)

Quiz

Weekly Quiz
  🔖 "Electricity Unit Week 5 Quiz" on SW pg. Q-23.

Quiz Answers
1. True
2. Central Processing Unit
3. Binary code
4. Answers will vary

Possible Schedules for Week 5

Two Days a Week Schedule	
Day 1	**Day 2**
❑ Read the first page from the Computers spread (Computers) ❑ Add information about computers and coding to the students' Narration Page ❑ Do the Scientific Demonstration: Coding ❑ Define binary code	❑ Read the second page from the Computers spread (Computers and Coding) ❑ Add information about computers and coding to the students' Narration Page ❑ Work on memorizing the *Electricity* poem ❑ Work on the Circuit Testing Project ❑ Give Electricity Week 5 quiz

Five Days a Week Schedule				
Day 1	**Day 2**	**Day 3**	**Day 4**	**Day 5**
❑ Do the Scientific Demonstration: Coding ❑ Define binary code ❑ Choose one or more of the additional books to read from this week	❑ Read the first page from the Computers spread (Computers) ❑ Add information about computers and coding to the students' Narration Page ❑ Complete the Secret Code Project	❑ Read the second page from the Computers spread (Computers and Coding) ❑ Add information about computers and coding to the students' Narration Page ❑ Complete the Binary Bracelet Project	❑ Complete the LEGO Coding Project ❑ Choose one or more of the additional books to read from this week	❑ Give Electricity Week 5 quiz ❑ Work on the Circuit Testing Project
All Week Long				
❑ Work on memorizing the *Electricity* poem				

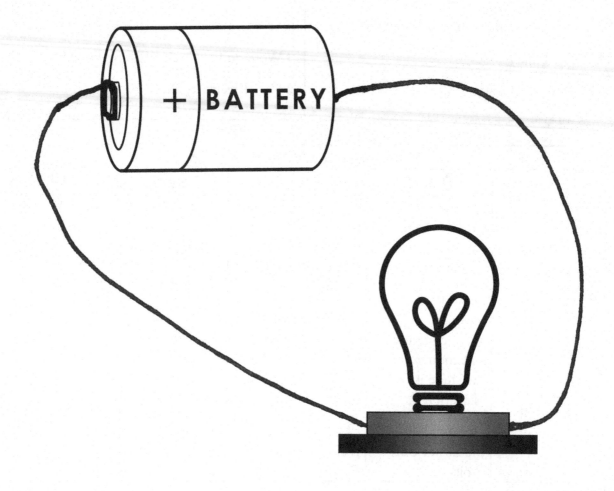

Physics for the Grammar Stage

Forces Unit

Forces Unit Overview
(5 weeks)

Books Scheduled
Required Encyclopedia
📖 *Usborne Children's Encyclopedia*
      OR
📖 *Usborne Children's Encyclopedia* and *DK Children's Encyclopedia*

Optional Additional Encyclopedia
📖 *Basher Science Physics: Why Matter Matters!*

Scientific Demonstrations Book
📖 *JVC Physics for Every Kid*

Sequence for Study
✍ **Week 1:** Forces
✍ **Week 2:** Balance
✍ **Week 3:** Gravity
✍ **Week 4:** Friction
✍ **Week 5:** Floating

Forces Unit Memory Work

Forces
A push or a pull is known as a force
When an object moves, a force is the source

Balance happens when all the forces still
This time push equals pull and objects chill

Visible forces make a real contact
Invisible ones, like in magnets act

That unseen force pulling you - gravity
The reason you fall in a cavity

Friction is a force that helps us to grip
It slows us down so that we do not slip

Look at the forces that act when boating
You will explain the physics of floating

Supplies Needed for the Unit

Week	Supplies needed
1	Toy car, String, Tape, Several books, Cardboard sheet
2	Pin, Index card, Scissors, Straw, 2 Blocks or cups of equal height, Ruler, Pen
3	Paper, Book (same size as the paper, but thicker)
4	String, Rubber band, 2 Large books, 10 round pencils or pens, Ruler
5	Large-mouth jar, Clear plastic tubing, Balloon
Unit Project	Washer, Box, Several shock-absorbing materials (e.g., newspaper, foam, cotton balls, or packing peanuts), String, Parachute materials (e.g., paper, fabric, or plastic wrap), 1 Qt container, Raw egg

Unit Vocabulary

1. **Force** – A push or pull on an object.
2. **Balance** – The point at which all the forces acting on an object cancel each other out.
3. **Resultant force** – The combined effect of the forces acting on an object.
4. **Gravity** – The pulling force that attracts objects to each other.
5. **Mass** – The amount of matter contained in an object.
6. **Weight** – A measure of the strength of the pull of gravity on an object.
7. **Friction** – The force that causes moving objects to slow down when they are touching.
8. **Lubricant** – A substance used to reduce friction.
9. **Density** – A measure of the amount of matter (mass) in a substance compared to its volume.

Week 1: Forces Lesson Plans

Scientific Demonstration: Forces Lab

Supplies Needed
- ✓ Toy car
- ✓ String
- ✓ Tape
- ✓ Several books
- ✓ Cardboard sheet

Purpose
This demonstration is meant to help the students see what forces do through two tests.

Instructions
1. Test #1 (Push): Set the car on a flat surface and observe what happens. Then, have the student gently push the back of the car and observe what happens.
2. Test #2 (Pull): Use the tape to attach a piece of string to the front of the car. Then, have the student gently pull on the string and observe what happens.
3. Test #3 (Both): On a smooth surface, stack several books on top of each other and then set the cardboard up against the books and the surface, creating a ramp. Hold the car at the top of the ramp and gently push it down the ramp, observing what happens.
4. Have the students write what they learn on the Lab Report on SW pg. 61.

Results and Explanation
The students should see that in each test, the car did not move until they either pushed or pulled the car. Their push or pull was a force that acted on the car causing it to move. In the third test, the car went even farther because of the push it was given plus the pull from gravity.

Take it Further
Have the students do another force-related demonstration - "Pendulum" on pp. 74-75 of *Janice VanCleave's Physics for Every Kid.*

Science-Oriented Books

Reading Assignments
- 📖 *Usborne Science Encyclopedia pp. 118-119 Forces*
- 📖 *Usborne Children's Encyclopedia pg. 194 Forces and DK pg. 108 Forces*

(Optional) Additional topics to explore this week: *Basher Physics pg. 20 Force*

Discussion Questions
After reading the selected pages, ask the following questions for your discussion time.

Forces
- ❓ What is a force?
- ❓ What are the different types of forces?

? What is a contact (or direct) force?

? How are forces measured?

(Optional) Additional Books

- 📖 *Forces Make Things Move (Let's-Read-and-Find-Out Science 2)* by Kimberly Bradley and Paul Meisel
- 📖 *Forces (Science Readers)* by Debra J. Housel
- 📖 *Push and Pull (Rookie Read-About Science)* by Patricia J. Murphy
- 📖 *Pushes and Pulls (TIME FOR KIDS® Nonfiction Readers)* by Sharon Coan

Notebooking

Writing Assignments

- ☐ **Narration Page –** Have the students dictate, copy, or write three to five sentences about forces on SW pg. 60. For example, this week the students could dictate, copy, or write the following:

    Forces are the pushes and pulls on an object. Forces can be things you see,
    such as pushing a car, or things you can't see, such as a magnet.
    A contact force is a force that needs two objects to touch each other.
    Forces are measured in Newtons.

- ☐ **(Optional) Lapbook –** Have the students begin the Forces and Motion lapbook by cutting out and coloring the cover on pg. 34. Then, have the students glue the sheet onto the front.

- ☐ **(Optional) Lapbook –** Have the students work on the Force Tab-book on pg. 35 of *Physics for the Grammar Stage Lapbooking Templates.* Have them cut out the force page and the cover page for the tab-book. Then, have the students color the pictures and add a sentence of two about forces on the force page. Have them put the pages in a safe place, as they will be adding to this tab-book throughout the unit.

Vocabulary

The following definition is a guide. The students' definition does not need to match word for word.

📖 **Force –** A push or a pull on an object. (SW pg. 108)

Multi-week Projects and Activities

Unit Project

✂ **Egg Drop Carrier –** Over this unit, the students will design and build a vessel to carry their egg as it is dropped from a height of at least six feet. This week, your students will test various shock absorbing materials. You will need a washer, a box, and several shock-absorbing materials, such as newspaper, foam, cotton balls, or packing peanuts. Begin by having the students drop the washer into the box and note the sound it makes. (*You can* *download a decibel meter app, if you would like to make your testing more scientific.*) Next, have the students line the box with one of the shock-absorbing materials. Again, drop the washer into the box and note any sound it makes on SW pg. 58. Then, have the students repeat the process for the remaining shock-absorbing materials.

Projects for this Week

✂ **Coloring Pages –** Have the students color the following pages from *Physics for the Grammar Stage Coloring Pages*: Forces pg. 30.

✂ **Force Balls –** Have the students do the "See for yourself" activity on pg. 118 of the *Usborne Science Encyclopedia*. You will need two balls and access to a smooth surface for this activity.

✂ **Invisible Force –** Have the students learn about invisible forces. You will need several metal paper clips (non-coated) and a magnet for this activity. Hold several paper clips in your hand and let go over a surface. What happens? (*The invisible force of gravity pulls the paper clips down to the surface.*) Then, hold the magnet just over one of the paper clips without touching it. What happens? (*The invisible force of magnetism pulls the paper clip up towards the magnet.*)

✂ **Force Race –** Have the students compete to see who can force a balloon over a line first. You will need an empty soda bottle and a balloon for each player. Begin by drawing two lines at either end of a room or outside. Then, give each player an empty soda bottle and a balloon. Have them line up on the first line. When you yell "go," the players will use their empty soda bottle to push their balloon towards the second line. The player to cross the line first wins the race.

Memorization

🗣 This week, begin working on memorizing the *Forces* poem. (SW pg. 124)

Quiz

Weekly Quiz

🖋 "Forces Unit Week 1 Quiz" on SW pg. Q-24.

Quiz Answers

1. A force is a push or a pull on an object.
2. False (*Forces can be visible, such as a contact force, or invisible, such as gravity.*)
3. Contact
4. Answers will vary

Possible Schedules for Week 1

Two Days a Week Schedule	
Day 1	**Day 2**
❑ Read the first page from the Forces spread (Forces) ❑ Add information about forces to the students' Narration Page ❑ Do the Scientific Demonstration: Forces Lab ❑ Work on memorizing the *Forces* poem ❑ Define force	❑ Read the second page from the Forces spread (Force) ❑ Add information about forces to the students' Narration Page ❑ Work on the Egg Drop Carrier Project ❑ Give Forces Week 1 quiz

Five Days a Week Schedule				
Day 1	**Day 2**	**Day 3**	**Day 4**	**Day 5**
❑ Do the Scientific Demonstration: Forces Lab ❑ Define force ❑ Choose one or more of the additional books to read from this week	❑ Read the first page from the Forces spread (Forces) ❑ Add information about forces to the students' Narration Page ❑ Complete the Force Balls Project	❑ Read the second page from the Forces spread (Force) ❑ Add information about forces to the students' Narration Page ❑ Complete the Invisible Forces Project	❑ Complete the Force Race Project ❑ Choose one or more of the additional books to read from this week	❑ Give Forces Week 1 quiz ❑ Work on the Egg Drop Carrier Project
All Week Long				
❑ Work on memorizing the *Forces* poem				

Week 2: Balance Lesson Plans

Scientific Demonstration: Straw Balance

Supplies Needed
- ✓ Pin
- ✓ Index card
- ✓ Scissors
- ✓ Straw
- ✓ 2 Blocks or cups of equal height
- ✓ Ruler
- ✓ Pen

Purpose
This demonstration is meant to help the students see how center of gravity affects balance.

Instructions and Explanation
The instructions and explanation for this scientific demonstration are found on pp. 84-85 of *Janice VanCleave's Physics for Every Kid*. Have the students complete the Lab Report on SW pg. 63.

Take it Further
Have the students do another balance-related demonstration - "Downward" on pg. 88-89 of *Janice VanCleave's Physics for Every Kid*.

Science-Oriented Books

Reading Assignments
- 📖 *Usborne Science Encyclopedia pg. 120 Combining Forces and Equilibrium*
- 📖 *Read the "Balance" article from pg. 190 of the Appendix to the students.*
- 📖 *Usborne Children's Encyclopedia pg. 195 Forces, part 2*

(Optional) Additional topics to explore this week: *No additional topics scheduled.*

Discussion Questions
After reading the selected pages, ask the following questions for your discussion time.

Balance
- ? What is the resultant force?
- ? What is equilibrium?
- ? When an object is sitting on a table, are there forces acting on it?
- ? In physics, what does it mean when an object is balanced?

(Optional) Additional Books
- 📖 *Balances (Science Tools)* by Adele D. Richardson
- 📖 *Make it Balance (Let's Explore Science)* by Claudette Williams

📖 *Balance (First Step Nonfiction Simple Tools)* by Sheila Rivera

Notebooking

Writing Assignments
- ☐ **Narration Page** – Have the students dictate, copy, or write three to five sentences on balance on SW pg. 62.
- ☐ **(Optional) Lapbook** – Have the students complete the Balance Mini-book on pg. 38 of *Physics for the Grammar Stage Lapbooking Templates*. Have them cut out and fold the template. Have the students color the pictures on the cover. Then, have the students add a sentence or two about balance on the inside. Finally, have them glue the mini-book into the lapbook.

Vocabulary
The following definitions are a guide. The students' definitions do not need to match word for word.
- ✏ **Balance** – The point at which all the forces acting on an object cancel each other out. (SW pg. 104)
- ✏ **Resultant force** – The combined effect of the forces acting on an object. (SW pg. 115)

Multi-week Projects and Activities

Unit Project
- ✂ **Egg Drop Carrier** – This week, the students will test out various materials to use a parachute. You will need string, a washer, and parachute materials, such as paper, fabric, or plastic wrap. For each material they are testing, have the students cut out an 8" by 8" square. Have them poke holes in the four corners of one of the squares. Then, have them cut out two 2 foot lengths of string and use these strings to attach the washer to the corners of the square, so that it hangs in the center. Once, the parachute is completed, have them hold out the washer at shoulder level and drop the washer. Have them record the time it takes for the washer to hit the ground and record it on SW pg. 58. Have the students repeat the process for the remaining parachute materials. Finally, have them drop just the washer and see how this compares to the parachute results.

Projects for this Week
- ✂ **Coloring Pages** – Have the students color the following pages from *Physics for the Grammar Stage Coloring Pages*: Balance pg. 31.
- ✂ **Card Balance** – Have the students do the "See for yourself" activity on pg. 109 of the *Usborne Science Encyclopedia*. You will need a hose and a cork for this activity.
- ✂ **Balancing Egg** – Have the students balance an egg on a table. You will need an egg, salt, and a flat surface. Start by making a small mound of salt on a hard, smooth, level surface. Then, have the students carefully balance the egg on top of the mound of salt and

gently blow the excess salt away. With patience and a steady hand, they should succeed in balancing the egg on its end. (*The egg is being supported by unseen salt crystals, which allow the egg to balance on its end effectively.*)

✂ **Balancing Robot –** Have the students make a balanced robot. You will need cardstock, scissors, 2 pennies, poster putty, and markers, crayons, or colored pencils. The directions and a free robot printable for this project can be found here:

🖱 https://buggyandbuddy.com/science-kids-balancing-robot-free-printable/

Memorization

🗣 This week, begin working on memorizing the *Forces* poem. (SW pg. 124)

Quiz

Weekly Quiz

🖊 "Forces Unit Week 2 Quiz" on SW pg. Q-25.

Quiz Answers

1. True
2. An object is in balance when all the forces that push or pull on it have caused it to remain still.
3. False (*When an object is at rest, there are still forces acting on it.*)
4. Answers will vary

Possible Schedules for Week 2

Two Days a Week Schedule	
Day 1	**Day 2**
❑ Read the Combing Forces and Equilibrium sections (Forces, part 2) ❑ Add information about balance to the students' Narration Page ❑ Do the Scientific Demonstration: Straw Balance ❑ Work on memorizing the *Forces* poem ❑ Define balance and resultant force	❑ Read the "Balance" article from the Appendix ❑ Add information about balance to the students' Narration Page ❑ Work on the Egg Drop Carrier Project ❑ Give Forces Week 2 quiz

Five Days a Week Schedule				
Day 1	**Day 2**	**Day 3**	**Day 4**	**Day 5**
❑ Do the Scientific Demonstration: Straw Balance ❑ Choose one or more of the additional books to read from this week	❑ Read the Combing Forces and Equilibrium sections (Forces, part 2) ❑ Add information about balance to the students' Narration Page ❑ Complete the Card Balance Project	❑ Read the "Balance" article from the Appendix ❑ Add information about balance to the students' Narration Page ❑ Complete the Balancing Egg Project	❑ Complete the Balance Robot Project ❑ Define balance and resultant force	❑ Give Forces Week 2 quiz ❑ Work on the Egg Drop Carrier Project
All Week Long				
❑ Work on memorizing the *Forces* poem				

Week 3: Gravity Lesson Plans

Scientific Demonstration: Same Speed

Supplies Needed
- ✓ Paper
- ✓ Book (same size as the paper, but thicker)

Purpose
This demonstration is meant to help the students see that gravity pulls all things down at the same speed.

Instructions and Explanation
The instructions and explanation for this scientific demonstration are found on pp. 72-73 of *Janice VanCleave's Physics for Every Kid*. Have the students complete the Lab Report on SW pg. 65.

Take it Further
Have the students do another gravity-related demonstration - "Up Hill" on pg. 68-69 of *Janice VanCleave's Physics for Every Kid*.

Science-Oriented Books

Reading Assignments
- 📖 *Usborne Science Encyclopedia pp. 130-131 Gravity*
- 📖 *Usborne Children's Encyclopedia pp. 198-199 Gravity and DK pg. 125 Gravity*

(Optional) Additional topics to explore this week: *Basher Physics pg. 26 Gravity, pg. 10 Mass, pg. 12 Weight.*

Discussion Questions
After reading the selected pages, ask the following questions for your discussion time.

Gravity
- **?** What is gravity?
- **?** How is mass related to gravity?
- **?** What is the difference between mass and weight?
- **?** What is an object's center of gravity?
- **?** How does gravity affect the earth and the moon?

(Optional) Additional Books
- 📖 *Gravity Is a Mystery (Let's-Read-and-Find-Out Science 2)* by Dr. Franklyn M. Branley and Edward Miller
- 📖 *Gravity (Blastoff! Readers: First Science)* by Kay Manolis
- 📖 *Gravity (First Step Nonfiction Forces and Motion)* by Robin Nelson
- 📖 *What Is Gravity? (Rookie Read-About Science)* by Lisa Trumbauer

📖 *You Wouldn't Want to Live Without Gravity!* by Anne Rooney and Mark Bergin

Notebooking

Writing Assignments

☐ **Narration Page** – Have the students dictate, copy, or write three to five sentences on gravity on SW pg. 64.

☐ **(Optional) Lapbook** – Have the students work on the Force Tab-book on pg. 36 of *Physics for the Grammar Stage Lapbooking Templates*. Have them cut out the gravity page and color the pictures. Then, have the students add a sentence of two about gravity, mass, and weight on the gravity page. Have them put the pages in a safe place, as they will be adding to this tab-book throughout the unit.

Vocabulary

The following definitions are a guide. The students' definitions do not need to match word for word.

✎ **Gravity** – The pulling force that attracts objects to each other. (SW pg. 109)

✎ **Mass** – The amount of matter contained in an object. (SW pg. 112)

✎ **Weight** – A measure of the strength of the pull of gravity on an object. (SW pg. 118)

Multi-week Projects and Activities

Unit Project

✂ **Egg Drop Carrier** – This week, have the students work on designing their egg drop carrier. They should use the knowledge they learned about shock-absorbing materials and parachutes over the last two weeks to design a carrier for their egg that will allow it to survive a six foot drop. They can sketch their plans in the diary on SW pg. 59, as the students will build their designs next week.

Projects for this Week

✂ **Coloring Pages** – Have the students color the following pages from *Physics for the Grammar Stage Coloring Pages*: Gravity pg. 32.

✂ **Gravity Painting** – Have the students use gravity to create a masterpiece. You will need several pom-poms, paper, and paint. Add a bit of water to the paint to thin it out a bit. Then, lay out a piece of paper on the floor. Have the students dip a pom-pom in paint and then drop it from should height onto the paper.

✂ **Center of Gravity** – Have the students do the "See for yourself" activity on pg. 131 of the *Usborne Science Encyclopedia*. You will need a piece of paper.

✂ **Bigger** – Have the students do another gravity-related demonstration - "Bigger" on pp. 70-71 of *Janice VanCleave's Physics for Every Kid*. For this activity you will need a plastic garbage bag, string, 2 small washers, scissors, and a ruler.

Memorization

🗣 This week, begin working on memorizing the *Forces* poem. (SW pg. 124)

Quiz

Weekly Quiz

🕯 "Forces Unit Week 3 Quiz" on SW pg. Q-26.

Quiz Answers

1. Gravity is the pulling force that attracts objects to each other.
2. Center of gravity
3. False (*Mass is the amount of matter in an object, while weight is the measure of the strength of the pull of gravity on an object.*)
4. Answers will vary

Possible Schedules for Week 3

Two Days a Week Schedule	
Day 1	**Day 2**
❏ Read the first page from the Gravity spread (Gravity) ❏ Add information about gravity to the students' Narration Page ❏ Do the Scientific Demonstration: Same Speed ❏ Work on memorizing the *Forces* poem ❏ Define gravity, mass, weight	❏ Read the second page from the Gravity spread (Gravity) ❏ Add information about gravity to the students' Narration Page ❏ Work on the Egg Drop Carrier Project ❏ Give Forces Week 3 quiz

Five Days a Week Schedule				
Day 1	**Day 2**	**Day 3**	**Day 4**	**Day 5**
❏ Do the Scientific Demonstration: Same Speed ❏ Choose one or more of the additional books to read from this week	❏ Read the first page from the Gravity spread (Gravity) ❏ Add information about gravity to the students' Narration Page ❏ Complete the Gravity Painting Project	❏ Read the second page from the Gravity spread (Gravity) ❏ Add information about gravity to the students' Narration Page ❏ Complete the Center of Gravity Project	❏ Complete the Bigger Project ❏ Define gravity, mass, weight	❏ Give Forces Week 3 quiz ❏ Work on the Egg Drop Carrier Project

All Week Long
❏ Work on memorizing the *Forces* poem

Week 4: Friction Lesson Plans

Scientific Demonstration: Roller

Supplies Needed
- ✓ String
- ✓ Rubber band
- ✓ 2 Large books
- ✓ 10 round pencils or pens
- ✓ Ruler

Purpose

This demonstration is meant to show the students how different surfaces affect friction.

Instructions and Explanation

The instructions and explanation for this scientific demonstration are found on pp. 156-157 of *Janice VanCleave's Physics for Every Kid*. Have the students complete the Lab Report on SW pg. 67.

Take it Further

Have the students do another friction-related demonstration - "How Far" on pg. 152-153 of *Janice VanCleave's Physics for Every Kid*.

Science-Oriented Books

Reading Assignments
- 📖 *Usborne Science Encyclopedia pp. 124-125 Friction*
- 📖 *Usborne Children's Encyclopedia pp. 202-203 Friction and DK pg. 114 Friction*

(Optional) Additional topics to explore this week: *Basher Physics pg. 24 Friction*

Discussion Questions

After reading the selected pages, ask the following questions for your discussion time.

Friction
- **?** What is friction?
- **?** How is friction useful?
- **?** How can we reduce friction?
- **?** What is air resistance (drag)?
- **?** What does it mean to streamline an object?

(Optional) Additional Books
- 📖 *Friction (True Books: Physical Science) by Matt Mullins*
- 📖 *Friction (Science Readers: Content and Literacy)* by Suzanne I. Barchers
- 📖 *What Is Friction? (Rookie Read-About Science)* by Lisa Trumbauer and David Larwa
- 📖 *Why Do Moving Objects Slow Down?: A Look at Friction* by Jennifer Boothroyd

Notebooking

Writing Assignments

☐ **Narration Page –** Have the students dictate, copy, or write three to five sentences on friction on SW pg. 66.

☐ **(Optional) Lapbook –** Have the students work on the Force Tab-book on pg. 36 of *Physics for the Grammar Stage Lapbooking Templates*. Have them cut out the friction page and color the pictures. Then, have the students add a sentence of two about friction and lubricants on the friction page. Have them put the pages in a safe place, as they will be adding to this tab-book throughout the unit.

Vocabulary

The following definitions are a guide. The students' definitions do not need to match word for word.

↷ **Friction –** The force that causes moving objects to slow down when they are touching. (SW pg. 108)

↷ **Lubricant –** A substance used to reduce friction. (SW pg. 111)

Multi-week Projects and Activities

Unit Project

✂ **Egg Drop Carrier –** This week, have the students work on building the egg drop carrier they designed the previous week. If they finish this week, have them take a picture and add it to their diary on SW pg. 59.

Projects for this Week

✂ **Coloring Pages –** Have the students color the following pages from *Physics for the Grammar Stage Coloring Pages*: Friction pg. 33.

✂ **Friction Block –** Have the students examine how different types of materials create more or less friction. You will need a 3 ft. section of a 2x4 board, a 1x2x4 block (average sized wooden block), a sheet of sandpaper, a washcloth, several large books, and a timer. Begin by propping up the board using the books so that the top is 18 inches higher than the bottom. Then, send the block down the board, recording the time it takes to get to the bottom. Next, cover the block with the washcloth and send it down the board, recording the time it takes to get to the bottom. Finally, cover the block with the sandpaper and send it down the board, recording the time it takes to get to the bottom. (*The students should see that it took longer for the block to go down the ramp on the second and third times, which is due to the friction caused by the washcloth and sandpaper. You can also have the students test out several lubricants to see if they speed up the block descent.*)

✂ **Friction Marbles –** Have the students do the "See for yourself" activity on pg. 125 of the *Usborne Science Encyclopedia*. You will need a book and some marbles for this activity.

✂ **Air Car –** Have the students do another friction-related demonstration - "Air Car" on pp. 158-159 of *Janice VanCleave's Physics for Every Kid*. For this activity you will need cardboard, a pencil, an empty thread spool, a balloon, ruler, scissors, glue, and notebook paper.

Memorization

This week, begin working on memorizing the *Forces* poem. (SW pg. 124)

Quiz

Weekly Quiz

"Forces Unit Week 4 Quiz" on SW pg. Q-27.

Quiz Answers

1. Friction is the force that causes moving objects to slow down when they are touching.
2. False (*A lubricant helps to reduce friction.*)
3. Air resistance (or drag)
4. True
5. Answers will vary

Possible Schedules for Week 4

Two Days a Week Schedule	
Day 1	Day 2
❑ Read the first page from the Friction spread (Friction) ❑ Add information about friction to the students' Narration Page ❑ Do the Scientific Demonstration: Roller ❑ Work on memorizing the *Forces* poem ❑ Define friction and lubricant	❑ Read the second page from the Friction spread (Friction) ❑ Add information about friction to the students' Narration Page ❑ Work on the Egg Drop Carrier Project ❑ Give Forces Week 4 quiz

Five Days a Week Schedule				
Day 1	Day 2	Day 3	Day 4	Day 5
❑ Do the Scientific Demonstration: Roller ❑ Choose one or more of the additional books to read from this week	❑ Read the first page from the Friction spread (Friction) ❑ Add information about friction to the students' Narration Page ❑ Complete the Friction Block Project	❑ Read the second page from the Friction spread (Friction) ❑ Add information about friction to the students' Narration Page ❑ Complete the Friction Marbles Project	❑ Complete the Air Car Project ❑ Define friction and lubricant	❑ Give Forces Week 4 quiz ❑ Work on the Egg Drop Carrier Project
All Week Long				
❑ Work on memorizing the *Forces* poem				

Week 5: Floating Lesson Plans

Scientific Demonstration: Bubbler

Supplies Needed
- ✓ Large-mouth jar
- ✓ Clear plastic tubing
- ✓ Balloon

Purpose
This demonstration is meant to help the students determine why bubbles rise in liquids.

Instructions and Explanation
The instructions and explanation for this scientific demonstration are found on pp. 60-61 of *Janice VanCleave's Physics for Every Kid*. Have the students complete the Lab Report on SW pg. 69.

Take it Further
Have the students do another buoyancy-related demonstration - "Rising Bottle" on pg. 58-59 of *Janice VanCleave's Physics for Every Kid*.

Science-Oriented Books

Reading Assignments
- 📖 *Usborne Science Encyclopedia pp. 138-139 Floating*
- 📖 *Usborne Children's Encyclopedia pg. 200-201 (Floating) and DK pg. 227 (Sinking and Floating)*

(Optional) Additional topics to explore this week: *Basher Physics pg. 14 Density*

Discussion Questions
After reading the selected pages, ask the following questions for your discussion time.

Floating
- **?** Why do things float?
- **?** What is Archimedes's principle?
- **?** What is density?
- **?** How does density relate to an object's ability to float?

(Optional) Additional Books
- 📖 *What Floats? What Sinks?: A Look at Density* by Jennifer Boothroyd
- 📖 *Dive! Dive! Dive!: Buoyancy (Raintree Fusion: Physical Science)* by Isabel Thomas

Notebooking

Writing Assignments
- ☐ **Narration Page –** Have the students dictate, copy, or write three to five sentences on

floating on SW pg. 68.

- ☐ **(Optional) Lapbook –** Have the students complete the Force Tab-book on pg. 37 of *Physics for the Grammar Stage Lapbooking Templates*. Have them cut out the density page and color the pictures. Then, have the students add a sentence of two about density on the density page. Once they are done, have them staple all the pages for the tab-book together and glue it into the lapbook.
- ☐ **(Optional) Lapbook –** Have the students complete the Floating Mini-book on pg. 39 of *Physics for the Grammar Stage Lapbooking Templates*. Have them cut out and fold the template. Have the students color the pictures on the cover. Then, have the students add a sentence or two about floating on the inside. Finally, have them glue the mini-book into the lapbook.

Vocabulary

The following definition is a guide. The students' definition does not need to match word for word.

- ✐ **Density –** A measure of the amount of matter (mass) in a substance compared to its volume. (SW pg. 107)

Multi-week Projects and Activities

Unit Project

- ✂ **Egg Drop Carrier –** This week, have the students finish the egg drop carrier project. Test the carriers by dropping them from the top of a ladder or from a second story window. (**Note**—*Be sure to take all necessary safety precautions so that no one is hurt during testing*.) Then, check the carriers to see what happened to the eggs! Afterwards, discuss what changes they could make to improve the egg drop carrier. You can ask the following questions:
  - **?** Would you use different materials next time?
  - **?** Would you use more or less of something?
  - **?** Do you have another idea for a carrier that could deliver an egg safely to the ground?

After you finish discussing these questions, have the students add a sentence or two to their egg drop carrier diary on SW pg. 59 sharing how they would change their design in the future.

Projects for this Week

- ✂ **Coloring Pages –** Have the students color the following pages from *Physics for the Grammar Stage Coloring Pages*: Floating pg. 34.
- ✂ **Floating Egg –** Have the students float an egg. You will need a cup, water, egg, and salt. Place an egg in a cup filled about two-thirds of the way with tap water and observe what happens. (*The students should see the egg sink to the bottom.*) Add about a quarter to a half a cup of salt, depending on the size of your glass. Stir gently and observe what happens

to the egg. (*The students should see the egg float. If it does not, you may need to add a bit more salt. The egg floats in the salt water because the liquid is more dense, which means that the egg weighs less than the salt water it displaces.*)

✂ **Floating Ball –** Have the students do the "See for yourself" activity on pg. 139 of the *Usborne Science Encyclopedia*. You will need modeling clay and a cup with water for this activity.

✂ **Floating Ship –** Have the students build a hovercraft. You will need a balloon, an old CD, a 2-L soda bottle lid, thin nail, and glue. Begin by using the nail to poke at least ten holes in the top of your soda bottle lid. Then, use the glue to attach the bottom of the lid over the hole in the center of the CD so that the holes face up. After the glue dries, set the CD on a table or flat surface and blow up the balloon. Quickly fit the balloon over the soda bottle lid and watch what happens! (*The CD will rise up just a bit and move across the table, just like a hovercraft. When the air is expelled from the balloon, it creates a cushion between the surface and the CD. This makes it possible for the CD-ship to float or hover over the surface. You can also repeat this experiment using a hair dryer on low instead, so that you can direct the movement of the CD-ship.*)

Memorization

🗣 This week, begin working on memorizing the *Forces* poem. (SW pg. 124)

Quiz

Weekly Quiz

🖊 "Forces Unit Week 5 Quiz" on SW pg. Q-28.

Quiz Answers

1. The same or less
2. True
3. Density is a measure of the amount of matter (mass) in a substance compared to its volume.
4. Answers will vary

Possible Schedules for Week 5

Two Days a Week Schedule	
Day 1	**Day 2**
❑ Read the first page from the Floating spread (Floating) ❑ Add information about floating to the students' Narration Page ❑ Do the Scientific Demonstration: Bubbler ❑ Work on memorizing the *Forces* poem ❑ Define density	❑ Read the second page from the Floating spread (Sinking and Floating) ❑ Add information about floating to the students' Narration Page ❑ Finish the Egg Drop Carrier Project ❑ Give Forces Week 5 quiz

Five Days a Week Schedule				
Day 1	**Day 2**	**Day 3**	**Day 4**	**Day 5**
❑ Do the Scientific Demonstration: Bubbler ❑ Define density	❑ Read the first page from the Floating spread (Floating) ❑ Add information about floating to the students' Narration Page ❑ Complete the Floating Egg Project	❑ Read the second page from the Floating spread (Sinking and Floating) ❑ Add information about floating to the students' Narration Page ❑ Complete the Floating Ball Project	❑ Complete the Floating Ship Project ❑ Choose one or more of the additional books to read from this week	❑ Give Forces Week 5 quiz ❑ Finish the Egg Drop Carrier Project

All Week Long

❑ Work on memorizing the *Forces* poem

Physics for the Grammar Stage

Motion Unit

Motion Unit Overview
(4 weeks)

Books Scheduled

Required Encyclopedia

📖 *Usborne Science Encyclopedia*
>   OR
📖 *There are no pages scheduled for this unit in the younger resources. Instead, we suggest that you either check out one or more of the library books suggested on the subjects or watch the suggested videos.*

Optional Additional Encyclopedia

📖 *Basher Science Physics: Why Matter Matters!*

Scientific Demonstrations Book

📖 *JVC Physics for Every Kid*

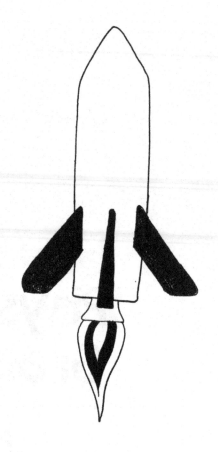

Sequence for Study

↻ **Week 1:** Dynamics
↻ **Week 2:** Motion
↻ **Week 3:** Circular Motion
↻ **Week 4:** Scientist Study - Isaac Newton

Motion Unit Memory Work

<u>Newton's Three Laws of Motion</u>

1. An object in motion will stay in motion and an object at rest will stay at rest unless they are acted on by an outside force.

2. The greater the force on an object, the greater the change in its motion. The greater the mass of an object, the greater the force needed to change its motion.

3. For every action, there is an equal but opposite reaction.

Supplies Needed for the Unit

Week	Supplies needed
1	Ruler, Straw, String, Scissors, Balloon, 2 Chairs, Tape

2	Table, 2 Books with the same thickness, Roll of masking tape, 2 Jar lids, Marble, Helper
3	3 Paper clips, Pencil, Notebook paper, Scissors, Ruler
4	*No supplies needed.*
Unit Project	Build-a-rocket kit

Unit Vocabulary

1. **Inertia** – The tendency of objects to resist a change in their movement.
2. **Momentum** – A measure of an object's tendency to continue moving.
3. **Acceleration** – A change in the speed or direction of an object.
4. **Speed** – A measure of how fast an object is moving.
5. **Centripetal force** – A force that keeps an object moving in a circle.
6. **Torque** – The force you add to make something rotate.

Week 1: Dynamics Lesson Plans

Scientific Demonstration: Balloon Rocket

Supplies Needed
- ✓ Ruler
- ✓ Straw
- ✓ String
- ✓ Scissors
- ✓ Balloon
- ✓ 2 Chairs
- ✓ Tape

Purpose
This demonstration is meant to help the students see one of Newton's Laws in action.

Instructions and Explanation
The instructions and explanation for this scientific demonstration are found on pp. 142-143 of *Janice VanCleave's Physics for Every Kid*. Have the students complete the Lab Report on SW pg. 75.

Take it Further
Have the students do another motion-related demonstration - "Paddle Boat" on pp. 160-161 of *Janice VanCleave's Physics for Every Kid*.

Science-Oriented Books

Reading Assignments
- 📖 *Usborne Science Encyclopedia pp. 122-123 Dynamics*
- 📖 *Video Suggestions:*
    - 🖱 3 Laws of Motion for Kids - https://www.youtube.com/watch?v=aA_mqSzbkM0
    - 🖱 What is momentum? - https://www.youtube.com/watch?v=y2Gb4NIv0Xg

(Optional) Additional topics to explore this week: *Basher Physics pg. 22 Inertia*

Discussion Questions
After reading the selected pages, ask the following questions for your discussion time.

Dynamics
- ? What is Newton's 1st law of motion?
- ? What is Newton's 2nd law of motion?
- ? What is Newton's 3rd law of motion?
- ? What is inertia?
- ? What is momentum?
- ? What does the law of conservation of momentum say?

(Optional) Additional Books

- 📖 *Motion (Science Readers: Content and Literacy)* by Debra Housel
- 📖 *And Everyone Shouted, "Pull!": A First Look at Forces and Motion* by Claire Llewellyn and Simone Abel
- 📖 *Motion: Push and Pull, Fast and Slow (Amazing Science)* by Darlene R. Stille and Sheree Boyd

Notebooking

Writing Assignments

- ☐ **Narration Page** – Have the students dictate, copy, or write three to five sentences about dynamics and Newton's Three laws of motion on SW pg. 74. For example, this week the students could dictate, copy, or write the following:

  > *Newton's first law of motion says that an object will stay in motion or at rest*
  > *unless a forces acts on it. Newton's second law of motion says the greater the force,*
  > *the greater the change in motion. Newton's third law of motion says that*
  > *for every action there is an equal, but opposite reaction.*
  > *The law of conservation of momentum says that the total momentum stays the same.*

- ☐ **(Optional) Lapbook** – Have the students complete the Three Laws of Motion Sheet on pg. 40 of *Physics for the Grammar Stage Lapbooking Templates*. Have them cut out the template and color the pictures. You can have the students copy the three laws of motion under their respective sections or cut out and glue on the pre-written laws. Once they are done, have them glue the sheet into the lapbook.

Vocabulary

The following definitions are a guide. The students' definitions do not need to match word for word.

- ✏️ **Inertia** – The tendency of objects to resist a change in their movement. (SW pg. 109)
- ✏️ **Momentum** – A measure of an object's tendency to continue moving. (SW pg. 112)

Multi-week Projects and Activities

Unit Project

- ✂️ **Rocket** – For this unit, the students will be building and launching a rocket. You will need a build-a-rocket kit, which you can purchase at Rainbow Resources or Amazon. We recommend getting one of the rocket kits by Estes that comes with the rocket pieces, a launch pad, and a rocket engine. (**Note**—*If you don't want to create an exploding rocket, we recommend the Stomp Rocket Kit.*) This week, have the students build and paint their rocket. After they are done, have them take a picture of it and add that to their rocket diary on SW pg. 72.

Projects for this Week

- ✂️ **Coloring Pages** – Have the students color the following pages from *Physics for the Grammar Stage Coloring Pages*: Newton's 1st Law pg. 35, Newton's 2nd Law pg. 36, Newton's 3rd Law pg. 37.

✂ **Inertia –** Have the students use inertia to get a penny into a glass. You will need an index card, a glass, and a penny. Set the index card over the glass and place the penny in the center. Quickly flick the index card so that it scoots off to the side of the glass, leaving the penny to drop into the glass. (*This may take a few tries to get exactly right, but once you figure out the trick, see how many pennies you can get into the glass at a time.*)

✂ **Momentum –** Have the students do the "See for yourself" activity on pg. 123 of the *Usborne Science Encyclopedia*. You will need a Newton's cradle for this activity.

✂ **Dynamic Marbles –** Have the students play a game of marbles. In the dynamic marble game, they will use one marble to hit and move another, which is a perfect example of the laws of motion! If you are not familiar with playing marbles, directions for this game can be found at the following website:

🖱 http://www.landofmarbles.com/marbles-play.html

Memorization

This week, begin working on memorizing *Newton's Three Laws of Motion*. (SW pg. 125)

Quiz

Weekly Quiz

⚑ "Motion Unit Week 1 Quiz" on SW pg. Q-29.

Quiz Answers

1. Inertia, momentum
2. True
3. Greater, greater
4. Action, opposite reaction
5. Answers will vary

Possible Schedules for Week 1

Two Days a Week Schedule	
Day 1	**Day 2**
❑ Read the first page from the Dynamics spread (Watch 1st Video)	❑ Read the second page from the Dynamics spread (Watch 2nd Video)
❑ Add information about dynamics to the students' Narration Page	❑ Add information about dynamics to the students' Narration Page
❑ Do the Scientific Demonstration: Balloon Rocket	❑ Work on memorizing *Newton's Three Laws of Motion*
❑ Define inertia and momentum	❑ Work on the Rocket Project
	❑ Give Motion Week 1 quiz

Five Days a Week Schedule				
Day 1	**Day 2**	**Day 3**	**Day 4**	**Day 5**
❑ Do the Scientific Demonstration: Balloon Rocket ❑ Define inertia and momentum	❑ Read the first page from the Dynamics spread (Watch Video) ❑ Add information about dynamics to the students' Narration Page ❑ Complete the Inertia Project	❑ Read the second page from the Dynamics spread ❑ Add information about dynamics to the students' Narration Page ❑ Complete the Momentum Project	❑ Complete the Dynamic Marbles Project ❑ Choose one or more of the additional books to read from this week	❑ Give Motion Week 1 quiz ❑ Work on the Rocket Project
All Week Long				
❑ Work on memorizing *Newton's Three Laws of Motion*				

Week 2: Motion Lesson Plans

Scientific Demonstration: Shake Up

Supplies Needed
- ✓ Table
- ✓ 2 Books with the same thickness
- ✓ Roll of masking tape
- ✓ 2 Jar lids
- ✓ Marble
- ✓ Helper

Purpose
This demonstration is meant to help the students see how shape affects speed.

Instructions and Explanation
The instructions and explanation for this scientific demonstration are found on pp. 78-79 of *Janice VanCleave's Physics for Every Kid*. Have the students complete the Lab Report on SW pg. 77.

Take it Further
Have the students repeat the demonstration using other sizes or shapes to transport the marbles.

Science-Oriented Books

Reading Assignments
- 📖 *Usborne Science Encyclopedia pp. 126-127 (Motion, part 2)*
- 📖 *Video Suggestions:*
  - 🖱 Speed and Velocity - https://youtu.be/DRb5PSxJerM
  - 🖱 Dr. Skateboard's Speed and Velocity - https://youtu.be/dKDDrnx-Fgw

(Optional) Additional topics to explore this week: *Basher Physics pg. 16 Speed, pg. 18 Acceleration*

Discussion Questions
After reading the selected pages, ask the following questions for your discussion time.

Motion
- **?** What do scientist look at when they study motion?
- **?** What is speed?
- **?** What is velocity?
- **?** What is acceleration? Deceleration?

(Optional) Additional Books
- 📖 *Motion (Blastoff! Readers: First Science)* by Kay Manolis
- 📖 *Vroom! Speed and Acceleration (TIME FOR KIDS® Nonfiction Readers)* by Stephanie Paris

📖 *Full Speed Ahead!: How Fast Things Go* by Cruschiform

Notebooking

Writing Assignments

- ☐ **Narration Page** – Have the students dictate, copy, or write three to five sentences on motion on SW pg. 76.
- ☐ **(Optional) Lapbook** – Have the students complete the Speed vs. Acceleration Shutterfold Book on pg. 41 of *Physics for the Grammar Stage Lapbooking Templates*. Have them cut the template for the shutterfold book and color the pictures. Next, have the students add a sentence about speed on the top of the inside. Then, have them add a sentence about acceleration on the bottom of the inside. Have them fold the mini-book and glue it into the lapbook.

Vocabulary

The following definitions are a guide. The students' definitions do not need to match word for word.

- ✏ **Acceleration** – A change in the speed or direction of an object. (SW pg. 104)
- ✏ **Speed** – A measure of how fast an object is moving. (SW pg. 117)

Multi-week Projects and Activities

Unit Project

- ✂ **Rocket** – This week, have the students launch their rockets. Have them take plenty of pictures to add to their diary. When they are done, have them write down their observations about their rocket's flight on SW pg. 72.

Projects for this Week

- ✂ **Coloring Pages** – Have the students color the following pages from *Physics for the Grammar Stage Coloring Pages*: Motion pg. 38.
- ✂ **Speed Ramps** – Have the students practice accelerating and decelerating a car. You will need a toy car, timer, and a ramp. Have the students set the car on a flat surface and gently push the car. Have them time how long it takes to stop. Then, have the push the car down the ramp and time how long it takes to stop. Finally, have the students push the car up the ramp and time how long it takes it to stop. (**Note**—*This should be the point at which it momentarily stops before heading back down the ramp.*) After the students are done, discuss what happened to the car during the three tests with them. (*In the first test, the car accelerated when a force acted on the car to change its speed and thanks to friction and air resistance the car decelerated till it came to a stop. In the second test the same principles apply as in the first test, but the acceleration was greater due to the ramp's downward direction. In the third test the same principles apply as in the first test, but the acceleration was diminished due to the ramp's upward direction.*)

✂ **Speed Drop –** Have the students do the "See for yourself" activity on pg. 127 of the *Usborne Science Encyclopedia*. You will need three balls of modeling clay for this activity.

✂ **Speed Poster –** Have the students make a poster depicting the differences between speed, velocity, and acceleration. Divide a piece of poster-board or paper into three sections. Begin by titling the first section "Speed" and add the definition of speed along with a picture of a ball in motion. Next, title the second section "Velocity" and add the definition of velocity along with a picture of a ball in motion and a arrow showing its direction. Finally, title the third section "Acceleration" and add the definition of acceleration along with a picture of a ball being hit by a bat. For your reference, you can use the following definition for velocity on the poster:

✎ **Velocity –** A measure of how fast an object is moving in a given direction.

Memorization

● This week, work on memorizing *Newton's Three Laws of Motion*. (SW pg. 125)

Quiz

Weekly Quiz

↳ "Motion Unit Week 2 Quiz" on SW pg. Q-30.

Quiz Answers

1. All of the above
2. True
3. Speed is a measure of how fast an object is moving.
4. Answers will vary

Possible Schedules for Week 2

Two Days a Week Schedule

Day 1	Day 2
❑ Read the first page from the Motion spread (Watch 1st Video)	❑ Read the second page from the Motion spread (Watch 2nd Video)
❑ Add information about speed to the students' Narration Page	❑ Add information about speed to the students' Narration Page
❑ Do the Scientific Demonstration: Shake Up	❑ Work on the Rocket Project
❑ Work on memorizing *Newton's Three Laws of Motion*	❑ Give Motion Week 2 quiz
❑ Define acceleration and speed	

Five Days a Week Schedule

Day 1	Day 2	Day 3	Day 4	Day 5
❑ Do the Scientific Demonstration: Shake Up ❑ Define acceleration and speed	❑ Read the first page from the Motion spread (Watch 1st Video) ❑ Add information about speed to the students' Narration Page ❑ Complete the Speed Races Project	❑ Read the second page from the Motion spread (Watch 2nd Video) ❑ Add information about speed to the students' Narration Page ❑ Complete the Speed Drop Project	❑ Complete the Speed Poster Project ❑ Choose one or more of the additional books to read from this week	❑ Give Motion Week 2 quiz ❑ Work on the Rocket Project

All Week Long

❑ Work on memorizing *Newton's Three Laws of Motion*

Week 3: Circular Motion Lesson Plans

Scientific Demonstration: Helicopter

Supplies Needed
- ✓ 3 Paper clips
- ✓ Pencil
- ✓ Notebook paper
- ✓ Scissors
- ✓ Ruler

Purpose
This demonstration is meant to help the students determine how weight affects the rotation speed of a paper helicopter.

Instructions and Explanation
The instructions and explanation for this scientific demonstration are found on pp. 148-149 of *Janice VanCleave's Physics for Every Kid*. Have the students complete the Lab Report on SW pg. 79.

Take it Further
Have the students do another circular motion-related demonstration - "Right or Left" on pp. 150-151 of *Janice VanCleave's Physics for Every Kid*.

Science-Oriented Books

Reading Assignments
- 📖 *Usborne Science Encyclopedia pp. 128-129 Motion, part 2*
- 📖 *Video Suggestions:*
  - 🎞 Centripetal Force - https://www.youtube.com/watch?v=KvCezk9DJfk
  - 🎞 What is centrifugal force? - https://www.youtube.com/watch?v=gRVIWWJwzfY

(Optional) Additional topics to explore this week: *No additional topics scheduled.*

Discussion Questions
After reading the selected pages, ask the following questions for your discussion time.

Circular Motion
- **?** What is terminal velocity?
- **?** What is true about objects moving in a circle?
- **?** What is centripetal force?
- **?** How does a gyroscope work?

(Optional) Additional Books
- 📖 *There are no additional books suggested for this week.*

Notebooking

Writing Assignments

- ☐ **Narration Page** – Have the students dictate, copy, or write three to five sentences on circular motion on SW pg. 78.
- ☐ **(Optional) Lapbook** – Have the students complete the Circular Motion Mini-book on pg. 42 of *Physics for the Grammar Stage Lapbooking Templates*. Have them cut out and fold the template. Have the students color the pictures on the cover. Then, have the students write the definition of centripetal force. Finally, have them glue the mini-book into the lapbook.

Vocabulary

The following definitions are a guide. The students' definitions do not need to match word for word.

- ↻ **Centripetal force** – A force that keeps an object moving in a circle. (SW pg. 105)
- ↻ **Torque** – The force you add to make something rotate. (SW pg. 117)

Multi-week Projects and Activities

Unit Project

- ✂ **Rocket** – This week, have the students think about what they could do to improve their rocket's flight. You can ask them the following questions:
    - ? Would you change the design of your fins on your rocket?
    - ? Would you use a different cone for your rocket?
    - ? Would a shorter or longer length improve your rocket design?

  Once, they come up with a few ideas, have them write those down on their rocket diary on SW pg. 73.

Projects for this Week

- ✂ **Coloring Pages** – Have the students color the following pages from *Physics for the Grammar Stage Coloring Pages*: Centripetal Force pg 39.
- ✂ **Circular Penny** – Have the students play with the circular motion of a penny. You will need a balloon and a penny for this activity. Place the penny inside the balloon, blow the balloon up, and tie the balloon off so that the penny won't come out. Now, give the balloon to the students and have them move it back and forth, up and down to get the penny rolling along the outside of the balloon. Then, stop and observe what happens. (*The penny will keep spinning around the balloon because of centripetal force.*)
- ✂ **Centripetal Marbles** – Have the students do the "See for yourself" activity on pg. 129 of the *Usborne Science Encyclopedia*. You will need a marble and a plastic bowl for this activity.
- ✂ **Spinning Shapes** – Have the students test different shapes to see how shape affects spin. You will need a sharpened pencil, thin cardboard, and scissors for this activity. Cut

out several shapes from the cardboard, such as a circle, a square, and a triangle. Mark the center of each shape and use the pointed end of the scissors to poke a hole in the center of each shape big enough for the pencil to fit through. Then, let the students test the spinning capabilities of each shape by seeing which one stays up the longest.

Memorization

🗣 This week, finish memorizing *Newton's Three Laws of Motion*. (SW pg. 125)

Quiz

Weekly Quiz

📌 "Motion Unit Week 3 Quiz" on SW pg. Q-31.

Quiz Answers

1. True
2. False (*Objects moving in a circle do travel in a straight line.*)
3. Centripetal force is a force that keeps an object moving in a circle.
4. Answers will vary

Possible Schedules for Week 3

Two Days a Week Schedule	
Day 1	Day 2
❏ Read the first page from the Motion, part 2 spread (Watch 1st Video)	❏ Read the first page from the Motion, part 2 spread (Watch 2nd Video)
❏ Add information about circular motion to the students' Narration Page	❏ Add information about circular motion to the students' Narration Page
❏ Do the Scientific Demonstration: Helicopter	❏ Finish the Rocket Project
❏ Work on memorizing *Newton's Three Laws of Motion*	❏ Give Motion Week 3 quiz
❏ Define centripetal force and torque	

Five Days a Week Schedule				
Day 1	Day 2	Day 3	Day 4	Day 5
❏ Do the Scientific Demonstration: Helicopter ❏ Define centripetal force and torque	❏ Read the first page from the Motion, part 2 spread (Watch 1st Video) ❏ Add information about circular motion to the students' Narration Page ❏ Complete the Circular Penny Project	❏ Read the first page from the Motion, part 2 spread (Watch 2nd Video) ❏ Add information about circular motion to the students' Narration Page ❏ Complete the Centripetal Marbles Project	❏ Complete the Spinning Shapes Project	❏ Give Motion Week 3 quiz ❏ Finish the Rocket Project
All Week Long				
❏ Work on memorizing *Newton's Three Laws of Motion*				

Week 4: Scientist Study - Isaac Newton

Science-Oriented Books

Reading Assignments

📖 *Who Was Isaac Newton?* by Janet B. Pascal

Over this week, the students will be reading *Who Was Isaac Newton?* You can purchase this book or you can get another book from the library. If you choose to get a different biography from the library, here are a few options:

📖 *Isaac Newton: The Scientist Who Changed Everything (National Geographic World History Biographies)* by Philip Steele
📖 *Isaac Newton (Giants of Science)* by Kathleen Krull and Boris Kulikov
📖 *Isaac Newton and the Laws of Motion* by Andrea Gianopoulos and Charles Barnett III

If you cannot find a suitable book on Isaac Newton at your library, you could look for a biography on one of the following scientists:

1. Thomas Edison - He was a famous American inventor.
2. Albert Einstein - He discovered E=mc², plus many other theories.
3. Niels Bohr - He applied quantum theory of physics to the structure of the atom.
4. William Gilbert - He was an English physicist who founded the study of magnetism.
5. Lord Kelvin (William Thomson) - He established the absolute temperature scale.

Assign the reading according to each student's skill level. In other words, if the students need two weeks to read the biography, take the extra time by moving the following weeks back and eliminating the additional biography assignment.

Discussion Questions

After reading the selected pages from the encyclopedias, ask the following questions in your discussion time:

? What was the title of the book you read?
? When and where was Isaac Newton born?
? What was his major scientific contribution?
? List the events that surround his discovery.
? List some other interesting events in the his life.
? Why do you think that it is important to learn about Isaac Newton?

Notebooking

Writing Assignments

☐ **Scientist Questionnaire –** Have the students fill in their answers to the questions about Isaac Newton on SW pp. 80-81.

☐ **(Optional) Scientist Report –** If you have older students, you may opt to have them write a short report on Isaac Newton. Have the students use their responses on the scientist questionnaire to write their rough draft. It should include an introductory paragraph, a paragraph on his scientific contributions, a paragraph on other interesting events in the scientist's life, and a conclusion that includes why they feel it is important to study that particular scientist. Have the students proofread and correct mistakes. Finally, have them give their reports a title and rewrite them as a final draft. Here are a few ideas to make their reports a bit more interesting:

1. Have the students turn their reports into a mini-book on the scientist, including pictures they have drawn.
2. Have the students make posters to present their reports.

Quiz

Weekly Quiz
↳ "Motion Unit Week 4 Quiz" on SW pg. Q-32.

Quiz Answers
1. Answers will vary

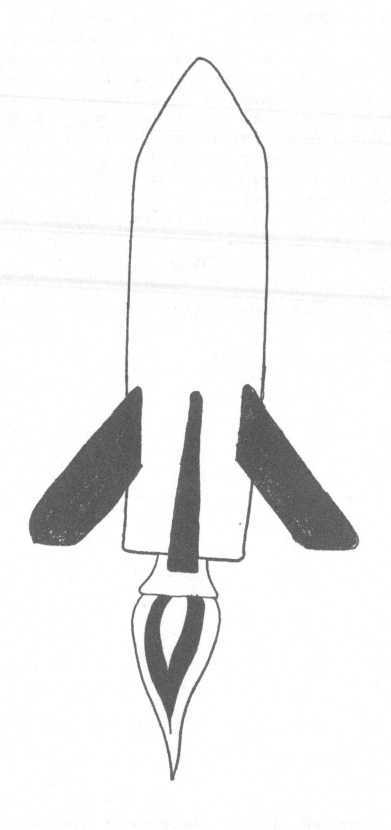

Physics for the Grammar Stage

Engineering Unit

Engineering Unit Overview
(8 weeks)

Books Scheduled

Required Encyclopedia
📖 *Basher Science Engineering: The Riveting World of Buildings and Machines*

Optional Additional Encyclopedia
📖 *Usborne Science Encyclopedia*

Scientific Demonstrations Book
📖 *JVC Physics for Every Kid*

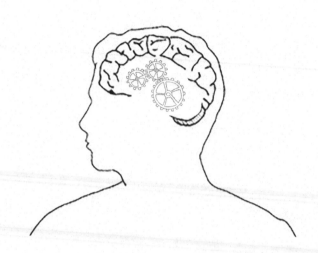

Sequence for Study
📖 **Week 1:** Ramps, Levers, and Screws
📖 **Week 2:** Gears, Pulleys, and Wheels
📖 **Week 3:** Turbines, Pumps, and Hydraulics
📖 **Week 4:** Engineering Design
📖 **Week 5:** Materials
📖 **Week 6:** Bridges and Arches
📖 **Week 7:** Modern Machines
📖 **Week 8:** Digital Machines

Engineering Unit Memory Work

Simple Machines
Simple machines are not complicated
But they help do the hard work dictated
Levers lift big loads through a fixed-point source
Screws turn motion into a driving force
Ramps allow moving up at a fast rate
Pulleys help to lift by spreading out weight
Gears change the speed simply by changing size
Wheels turn around a rod and the load flies
All these modest machines move loads along
They help us to do hard work and look strong

The Engineering Design Process
The design all begins with an engineer
Who sees a problem or need appear
And questions and researches to be sure
Now, the design goal - no longer obscure

Brainstorming begins, ideas written out
The best one is selected to tryout
The top drawing is built and created
A new prototype is designated
Testing begins and if the design fails
The engineer learns from the test details
The prototype redesigned with much heed
Until the engineer meets the first need

Supplies Needed for the Unit

Week	Supplies needed
1	4 Books, 2 Pencils
2	Empty thread spool, 2 Pencils, String, Scissors, 2 Paper cups, 20 Pennies, Pen
3	Eyedropper, Poster board, Toothpick, Scissors
4	Ruler, Pencil, 30 Pennies
5	Cornstarch, Water, Vegetable Oil, Plastic baggie, Food coloring
6	Air dry clay, Pack of pipe cleaners, Plastic cup, Pennies
7	Sheet of paper, Scissors, String, Ruler, Tape
8	Smartphone or GPS device, Geo-caching app
Unit Project	K'nex Gears Kit, Paper, Masking tape, Several newspapers

Unit Vocabulary

1. **Load** – The force of an object's weight that a machine needs to overcome.
2. **Simple Machine** – A device, such as a lever or a pulley, that helps to multiply the effort in order to move a load.
3. **Work** – Something that is done when a force moves an object.
4. **Engine** – A machine that converts stored energy into movement.
5. **Engineer** – A person who uses science and math to design products and processes that meet needs and solve problems.
6. **Prototype** – A working model that allows engineers to test their idea.
7. **Infrastructure** – A system of roads, bridges, tunnels, and fundamental services that make it possible for us to live in cities and towns.
8. **Buoyancy** – The way an object sinks or floats in either air or water.
9. **Robot** – A machine that does routine tasks on command.

Week 1: Ramps, Levers, and Screws Lesson Plans

Scientific Demonstration: Levers

Supplies Needed
- ✓ 4 Books
- ✓ 2 Pencils

Purpose
This demonstration is meant to help the students see the effectiveness of a lever.

Instructions and Explanation
The instructions and explanation for this scientific demonstration are found on pp. 118-119 of *Janice VanCleave's Physics for Every Kid*. Have the students complete the Lab Report on SW pg. 89.

Take it Further
Have the students do another ramp-related demonstration - "Weakling" on pp. 120-121 of *Janice VanCleave's Physics for Every Kid*.

Science-Oriented Books

Reading Assignments
- *Basher Engineering pg. 32 Ramp, pg. 34 Lever, pg. 44 Screw*

(Optional) Additional topics to explore this week: *Usborne Science Encyclopedia pg. 134 Simple Machines*

Discussion Questions
After reading the selected pages, ask the following questions for your discussion time.

Ramps
- ? What is the job of a ramp?
- ? How does a ramp work?

Levers
- ? What is the job of a lever?
- ? How does a lever work?

Screws
- ? What is a screw?
- ? What do screws do?

(Optional) Additional Books
- *Roll, Slope, and Slide: A Book About Ramps (Amazing Science: Simple Machines)* by Michael Dahl and Denise Shea
- *Ramps (Simple Machines: Blastoff Readers, Level 4)* by Kay Manolis
- *Levers (Simple Machines: Blastoff Readers, Level 4)* by Kay Manolis
- *Levers in Action (Simple Machines at Work)* by Gillian Gosman

📖 *Screws (Simple Machines)* by Martha E. H. Rustad

📖 *Screws (Blastoff! Readers: Simple Machines, Level 4)* by Kay Manolis

Notebooking

Writing Assignments

☐ **Narration Page –** Have the students dictate, copy, or write three to five sentences about ramps, levers, and screws on SW pg. 88. For example, this week the students could dictate, copy, or write the following:

> *The job of a ramp is to help you lift a load uphill. A ramp helps to break the work of lifting a load into smaller steps. The job of a lever is to transmit force. A lever turns at a fixed point or pivot to help lift the load. A screw is a ramp twisted around an axle. Screws are used to fasten, drill, and move loads.*

☐ **(Optional) Lapbook –** Have the students complete the Inclined Planes, Levers, and Screws Tab-book on pg. 45 of *Physics for the Grammar Stage Lapbooking Templates*. Have them cut out the template pages. Have the students color the picture on the cover. Then, have the students write the definition of an inclined plane on the Inclined Planes page. Repeat this process for the Levers and Screws pages. Finally, have them staple the pages together and glue the mini-book into the lapbook.

Vocabulary

The following definitions are a guide. The students' definitions do not need to match word for word.

✐ **Load –** The force of an object's weight that a machine needs to overcome. (SW pg. 111)

✐ **Simple Machine –** A device, such as a lever or a pulley, that helps to multiply the effort in order to move a load. (SW pg. 116)

Multi-week Projects and Activities

Unit Project

✂ **Building Projects –** For this project, you will need a K'nex: Intro to Simple Machines: Gears Kit or a comparable building kit that contains the materials for at least 7 projects relating to simple machines. You can purchase the K'nex kit at Rainbow Resources, CBD, Home Science Tools, or Amazon. Each week, your students will choose one project to complete. After they are done, take a picture of what they created and add the photo, along with a sentence or two of what they learned, to the Building Projects Diary in the SW on pp. 84. This week, we recommend trying the Eggbeater project.

Projects for this Week

✂ **Coloring Pages –** Have the students color the following pages from *Physics for the Grammar Stage Coloring Pages*: Ramp pg. 40, Lever pg. 41, Screw pg. 42.

✂ **Inclined –** Have the students do the demonstration entitled "Inclined" on pp. 114-115 of

Janice VanCleave's Physics for Every Kid. You will need string, a rubber band, two books, a bottle of glue, and a ruler for this activity.

✂ **Simple Machines Poster –** Have the students create a collage of all the simple machines they learn about over the next three weeks. This week, have them add examples of ramps, levers, and screws to the top third of a sheet of poster-board. They can draw the simple machines or use magazine pictures to represent the simple machines. If you would like, you can also have them add a sentences or two about each one.

✂ **Lifter –** Have the students do the demonstration entitled "Lifter" on pp. 110-111 of *Janice VanCleave's Physics for Every Kid.* You will need a large screw for this activity.

Memorization

This week, begin working on memorizing the *Simple Machines* poem. (SW pg. 126)

Quiz

Weekly Quiz

"Engineering Unit Week 1 Quiz" on SW pg. Q-33.

Quiz Answers

1. A simple machine is a device, such as a lever or a pulley, that helps to multiple]y the effort in order to move a load.
2. Load
3. C,A,B
4. Answers will vary

Possible Schedules for Week 1

Two Days a Week Schedule

Day 1	Day 2
❏ Read the page on Levers ❏ Add information about levers to the students' Narration Page ❏ Do the Scientific Demonstration: Levers ❏ Define load and simple machines ❏ Work on memorizing the *Simple Machines* poem	❏ Read the pages on Ramps and Screws ❏ Add information about ramps and screws to the students' Narration Page ❏ Work on one of the Building Projects ❏ Give Engineering Week 1 quiz

Five Days a Week Schedule

Day 1	Day 2	Day 3	Day 4	Day 5
❏ Read the page on Ramps ❏ Add information about ramps to the students' Narration Page ❏ Complete the Inclined Project	❏ Read the page on Levers ❏ Add information about levers to the students' Narration Page ❏ Complete the Simple Machines Poster Project	❏ Do the Scientific Demonstration: Levers ❏ Define load and simple machines ❏ Choose one or more of the additional books to read from this week	❏ Read the page on Screws ❏ Add information about screws to the students' Narration Page ❏ Complete the Lifter Project	❏ Give Engineering Week 1 quiz ❏ Work on one of the Building Projects

All Week Long

❏ Work on memorizing the *Simple Machines* poem

Week 2: Wheels, Gears, and Pulleys Lesson Plans

Scientific Demonstration: Wheel and Axle

Supplies Needed
- ✓ Empty thread spool
- ✓ 2 Pencils
- ✓ String
- ✓ Scissors
- ✓ 2 Paper cups
- ✓ 20 Pennies
- ✓ Pen

Purpose
This demonstration is meant to help the students see how a wheel and axle can help make work easier.

Instructions and Explanation
The instructions and explanation for this scientific demonstration are found on pp. 124-125 of *Janice VanCleave's Physics for Every Kid*. Have the students complete the Lab Report on SW pg. 91.

Take it Further
Have the students choose to do another simple machine-related demonstration - "Wedge" on pp. 112-113 of *Janice VanCleave's Physics for Every Kid*.

Science-Oriented Books

Reading Assignments
📖 *Basher Engineering pg. 36 Wheel and Axle, pg. 38 Gears and Belts, pg. 40 Pulley*
(Optional) Additional topics to explore this week: *Usborne Science Encyclopedia pg. 135 Simple Machines*

Discussion Questions
After reading the selected pages, ask the following questions for your discussion time.

Wheels
❓ What is the job of a wheel and axle?
❓ How do a wheel and axle work together?

Gears
❓ What is the job of a gear?
❓ How do gears work?

Pulleys
❓ How does a pulley work?
❓ What is a pulley made from?

(Optional) Additional Books

- *Wheels and Axles (Simple Machines)* by Martha E. H. Rustad
- *Gears Go, Wheels Roll (Science Starts)* by Mark Weakland
- *Pulleys and Gears (Simple Machines)* by David Glover
- *Pull, Lift, and Lower: A Book About Pulleys* by Michael Dahl and Denise Shea
- *Simple Machines: Wheels, Levers, and Pulleys* by David A. Adler and Anna Raff

Notebooking

Writing Assignments

- ☐ **Narration Page –** Have the students dictate, copy, or write three to five sentences on wheels, gears, and pulleys on SW pg. 90.
- ☐ **(Optional) Lapbook –** Have the students complete the Gears, Pulleys, and Wheels Wheel-book on pg. 46 of *Physics for the Grammar Stage Lapbooking Templates*. Have them cut out the wheel templates. On the third of the wheel with the gear picture, have the students write the definition of a gear. On the third of the wheel with the pulley picture, have the students write the definition of a pulley. On the third of the wheel with the wheel picture, have the students write the definition of a wheel. Then, use a brad to attach the two pages together so that the cover spins to reveal one part at a time. Finally, have them glue the mini-book into the lapbook.

Vocabulary

The following definition is a guide. The students' definition does not need to match word for word.

- ✎ **Work –** Something that is done when a force moves an object. (SW pg. 118)

Multi-week Projects and Activities

Unit Project

- ✂ **Building Projects –** Have the students build one of the projects from the K'nex: Intro to Simple Machines: Gears Kit. After they are done, take a picture of what they created and add the photo, along with a sentence or two of what they learned, to the Building Projects Diary in the SW on pp. 84. This week, we recommend trying the Chainsaw project.

Projects for this Week

- ✂ **Coloring Pages –** Have the students color the following pages from *Physics for the Grammar Stage Coloring Pages*: Wheel and Axle pg. 43, Gears pg. 44, Pulleys pg. 45.
- ✂ **Simple Machines Lab –** Have the students build and test several simple machines. You will need a thick, heavy book, round pencils, a block of wood, a nail, a screw, a brick or concrete block, and a wooden board for this activity. Directions for this project can be found here:
  - ✍ https://elementalscience.com/blogs/science-activities/3-ideas-for-building-simple-

160

machines-at-home

✂ **Ribbon Wench –** Have the students build and test their own ribbon wench. You will need two paper towel tubes, a spool of ribbon, a straw, string, tape, scissors, and a small basket for this activity. Directions for this project can be found here:

🖱 https://littlebinsforlittlehands.com/build-a-winch-simple-machine-recycled-stem-activity/

✂ **Simple Machines Poster –** Have the students continue to work on the simple machine collage they started last week. This week, have them add examples of wheels, gears, and pulleys to the middle third of a sheet of poster-board. They can draw the simple machines or use magazine pictures to represent the simple machines. If you would like, you can also have them add a sentences or two about each one.

Memorization

🗣 This week, continue working on memorizing the *Simple Machines* poem. (SW pg. 126)

Quiz

Weekly Quiz

🔩 "Engineering Unit Week 2 Quiz" on SW pg. Q-34.

Quiz Answers

1. B,C,A
2. Work is something that is done when a force moves an object.
3. Answers will vary

Possible Schedules for Week 2

Two Days a Week Schedule	
Day 1	**Day 2**
❑ Read the page on Wheels and Axles	❑ Read the pages on Gears and Pulleys
❑ Add information about wheels and axles to the students' Narration Page	❑ Add information about gears and pulleys to the students' Narration Page
❑ Do the Scientific Demonstration: Wheel and Axles	❑ Define work
❑ Work on memorizing the *Simple Machines* poem	❑ Work on one of the Building Projects
	❑ Give Engineering Week 2 quiz

Five Days a Week Schedule				
Day 1	**Day 2**	**Day 3**	**Day 4**	**Day 5**
❑ Read the page on Wheels and Axles ❑ Add information about wheels and axles to the students' Narration Page ❑ Complete the Simple Machines Lab Project	❑ Do the Scientific Demonstration: Wheel and Axles ❑ Define work ❑ Choose one or more of the additional books to read from this week	❑ Read the page on Gears ❑ Add information about gears to the students' Narration Page ❑ Complete the Ribbon Wench Project	❑ Read the page on Pulleys ❑ Add information about pulleys to the students' Narration Page ❑ Complete the Simple Machines Poster Project	❑ Give Engineering Week 2 quiz ❑ Work on one of the Building Projects
All Week Long				
❑ Work on memorizing the *Simple Machines* poem				

Week 3: Turbines, Pumps, and Hydraulics Lesson Plans

Scientific Demonstration: Pumps

Supplies Needed
- ✓ Eyedropper
- ✓ Poster board
- ✓ Toothpick
- ✓ Scissors

Purpose
This demonstration is meant to help the students see how a wheel can be used as a pump.

Instructions and Explanation
The instructions and explanation for this scientific demonstration are found on pp. 116-117 of *Janice VanCleave's Physics for Every Kid*. Have the students complete the Lab Report on SW pg. 93.

Take it Further
Have the students do another simple machine-related demonstration - "Tug-o-war" on pp. 126-127 of *Janice VanCleave's Physics for Every Kid*.

Science-Oriented Books

Reading Assignments
📖 *Basher Engineering pg. 42 Turbine, pg. 46 Pump, pg. 48 Hydraulics*
(Optional) Additional topics to explore this week: *Usborne Science Encyclopedia pg. 137 Using Simple Machines, pp. 146–150 Engines*

Discussion Questions
After reading the selected pages, ask the following questions for your discussion time.

Turbine
? What do turbines do?
? What is an example of a turbine?

Pump
? What do pumps do?
? How do pumps work?

Hydraulics
? How do hydraulics transmit forces?
? What makes hydraulics special?

(Optional) Additional Books
📖 *Simple Machines (Let's-Read-and-Find-Out Science 2)* by D. J. Ward and Mike Lowery
📖 *Simple Machines: Real Size Science* by Rebecca Rissman
📖 *Simple Machines (Rookie Read–About Science)* by Allan Fowler

📖 *How Machines Work: Zoo Break!* by David Macaulay

Notebooking

Writing Assignments
- ☐ **Narration Page –** Have the students dictate, copy, or write three to five sentences on turbines, pumps, and hydraulics on SW pg. 92.
- ☐ **(Optional) Lapbook –** Have the students complete the Hydraulics, Pumps, and Turbines Tab-book on pg. 47 of *Physics for the Grammar Stage Lapbooking Templates*. Have them cut out the template pages. Have the students color the picture on the cover. Then, have the students write what hydraulics do on the Hydraulics page. Repeat this process for the Pumps and Turbines pages. Finally, have them staple the pages together and glue the mini-book into the lapbook.

Vocabulary
The following definition is a guide. The students' definition does not need to match word for word.
- ✏️ **Engine –** A machine that converts stored energy into movement. (SW pg. 108)

Multi-week Projects and Activities

Unit Project
- ✂️ **Building Projects –** Have the students build one of the projects from the K'nex: Intro to Simple Machines: Gears Kit. After they are done, take a picture of what they created and add the photo, along with a sentence or two of what they learned, to the Building Projects Diary in the SW on pp. 85. This week, we recommend trying the Blender project.

Projects for this Week
- ✂️ **Coloring Pages –** Have the students color the following pages from *Physics for the Grammar Stage Coloring Pages*: Turbines pg. 46, Pumps pg. 47, Hydraulics pg. 48.
- ✂️ **Engines –** Have the students learn a bit more about engines, which can use turbines, pumps, and hydraulics to do work. Read *Usborne Science Encyclopedia pp. 146-149 (Engines)* and then have the students choose one of the "See for Yourself" activities to try out.
- ✂️ **Simple Machines Poster –** Have the students continue to work on the simple machine collage they started last week. This week, have them add examples of hydraulics, pumps, and turbines to the bottom third of a sheet of poster-board. They can draw the simple machines or use magazine pictures to represent the simple machines. If you would like, you can also have them add a sentences or two about each one.
- ✂️ **Simple Pneumatic Machine –** Have the students build and test a simple pneumatic machine. You will need 9 craft sticks, 5 jumbo craft sticks, 2 straws, 1 pipe cleaner, 2 10ml

Leur slip syringes, 6" of tubing, and masking tape for this activity. Directions for this project can be found here:

🖰 http://www.instructables.com/id/Simple-Pneumatic-Machine/

Memorization

🗣 This week, continue working on memorizing the *Simple Machines* poem. (SW pg. 126)

Quiz

Weekly Quiz

🔖 "Engineering Unit Week 3 Quiz" on SW pg. Q-35.

Quiz Answers

1. Curved blades, movement
2. True
3. Force
4. Answers will vary

Possible Schedules for Week 3

Two Days a Week Schedule	
Day 1	Day 2
❑ Read the page on Pumps ❑ Add information about pumps to the students' Narration Page ❑ Do the Scientific Demonstration: Pumps ❑ Work on memorizing the *Simple Machines* poem	❑ Read the page on Turbines and Hydraulics ❑ Add information about turbines and hydraulics to the students' Narration Page ❑ Define engine ❑ Work on one of the Building Projects ❑ Give Engineering Week 3 quiz

Five Days a Week Schedule				
Day 1	Day 2	Day 3	Day 4	Day 5
❑ Read the page on Turbines ❑ Add information about turbines to the students' Narration Page ❑ Define engine ❑ Complete the Engine Project	❑ Read the page on Pumps ❑ Add information about pumps to the students' Narration Page ❑ Complete the Simple Machines Poster Project	❑ Do the Scientific Demonstration: Pumps ❑ Choose one or more of the additional books to read from this week	❑ Read the page on Hydraulics ❑ Add information about hydraulics to the students' Narration Page ❑ Complete the Simple Pneumatic Machine Project	❑ Give Engineering Week 3 quiz ❑ Work on one of the Building Projects
All Week Long				
❑ Work on memorizing the *Simple Machines* poem				

Week 4: Engineering Design Lesson Plans

Scientific Demonstration: Best Spot

Supplies Needed
- ✓ Ruler
- ✓ Pencil
- ✓ 30 Pennies

Purpose
This demonstration is meant to help the students to engineer the best spot for a lever's fixed point.

Instructions and Explanation
The instructions and explanation for this scientific demonstration are found on pp. 122-123 of *Janice VanCleave's Physics for Every Kid*. Have the students complete the Lab Report on SW pg. 95.

Take it Further
Have the students repeat the experiment, but this time use a thicker dowel rod in place of the pencil. Let the students see how this change affects the results.

Science-Oriented Books

Reading Assignments
- 📖 Article: "The Engineering Design Process" *on Appendix pg. 191*
- 📖 *Basher Engineering pg. 56 Prototype*

(Optional) Additional topics to explore this week: *Basher Engineering pg. 52 Ergonomics, pg. 54 Blueprint*

Discussion Questions
After reading the selected pages, ask the following questions for your discussion time.

Engineering Design
- **?** What does an engineer do?
- **?** What are the design steps that an engineer follows?

Prototype
- **?** What is a prototype?
- **?** What is the purpose of a prototype?

(Optional) Additional Books
- 📖 *Engineers Solve Problems (Engineering Close-Up)* by Reagan Sikkens Miller
- 📖 *Rosie Revere's Big Project Book for Bold Engineers* by Andrea Beaty and David Roberts

Notebooking

Writing Assignments

- ☐ **Narration Page –** Have the students dictate, copy, or write three to five sentences on the engineering design process on SW pg. 94.
- ☐ **(Optional) Lapbook –** Have the students complete the Engineering Design Process Sheet on pg. 48 of *Physics for the Grammar Stage Lapbooking Templates*. Have them cut out the sheet and color the picture. Then, have the students add the eight steps under the appropriate numbers. Here are the steps, for your reference:
    1. Identify the need or problem
    2. Do research
    3. Define the design goal
    4. Brainstorm for ideas
    5. Select the best idea
    6. Build a prototype
    7. Test the prototype
    8. Redesign as needed

  After they are done, have the students glue the sheet into the lapbook.

Vocabulary

The following definitions are a guide. The students' definitions do not need to match word for word.

- ✎ **Engineer –** A person who uses science and math to design products and processes that meet needs and solve problems. (SW pg. 108)
- ✎ **Prototype –** A working model that allows engineers to test their idea. (SW pg. 113)

Multi-week Projects and Activities

Unit Project

- ✂ **Building Projects –** Have the students build one of the projects from the K'nex: Intro to Simple Machines: Gears Kit. After they are done, take a picture of what they created and add the photo, along with a sentence or two of what they learned, to the Building Projects Diary in the SW on pp. 85. This week, we recommend trying the Stationary Bike project.

Projects for this Week

- ✂ **Coloring Pages –** Have the students color the following pages from *Physics for the Grammar Stage Coloring Pages*: Engineer pg 49.
- ✂ **Engineering Design Poster –** Have the students make a poster depicting the eight steps of the engineering design process.
- ✂ **Engineers –** Have the students watch the following video on the what engineers do:
    - 🖱 https://www.youtube.com/watch?v=D9I35Rqo04E

✄ **Engineering a Tower** – Have the students engineer a tower. You will need a container of floss, 25 strands of uncooked spaghetti, and a bunch of cotton balls. Have the students design and build a tower out of the uncooked spaghetti, using the floss to hold the strands together. The tower should have a place at the top that can hold several cotton balls. If you have several students and want to make this a contest, give the students a thirty minute time limit for designing and building their structures.

Memorization

This week, continue working on memorizing the *Simple Machines* poem. (SW pg. 126)

Quiz

Weekly Quiz

"Engineering Unit Week 4 Quiz" on SW pg. Q-36.

Quiz Answers

1. 7,3,1,5,2,6,8,4
2. Prototype
3. Answers will vary

Possible Schedules for Week 4

Two Days a Week Schedule	
Day 1	**Day 2**
❑ Read the article "The Engineering Design Process" ❑ Add information about engineering design to the students' Narration Page ❑ Do the Scientific Demonstration: Best Spot ❑ Work on memorizing the *Simple Machines* poem	❑ Read the first page on Prototypes ❑ Add information about prototypes to the students' Narration Page ❑ Define engineer and prototype ❑ Work on one of the Building Projects ❑ Give Engineering Week 4 quiz

Five Days a Week Schedule				
Day 1	**Day 2**	**Day 3**	**Day 4**	**Day 5**
❑ Do the Scientific Demonstration: Best Spot ❑ Choose one or more of the additional books to read from this week	❑ Read the article "The Engineering Design Process" ❑ Add information about engineering design to the students' Narration Page ❑ Complete the Engineering Design Poster Project	❑ Read the first page on Prototypes ❑ Add information about prototypes to the students' Narration Page ❑ Watch the Engineers Video	❑ Work on the Engineering a Tower Project ❑ Define engineer and prototype ❑ Choose one or more of the additional books to read from this week	❑ Give Engineering Week 4 quiz ❑ Work on one of the Building Projects
All Week Long				
❑ Work on memorizing the *Simple Machines* poem				

Week 5: Materials Lesson Plans

Scientific Demonstration: Bioplastic

Supplies Needed
- ✓ Cornstarch
- ✓ Water
- ✓ Vegetable Oil
- ✓ Plastic baggie
- ✓ Food coloring

Purpose
This demonstration is meant to help the students to see how to make a plastic-like material from kitchen ingredients.

Instructions
1. In the bag, mix 3 tablespoons of cornstarch, 3 tablespoons of water, 8 to 10 drops of vegetable oil, and a few drops of food coloring.
2. Have the students mix the ingredients up thoroughly.
3. Then, seal the bag halfway, place it on a plate, and place the bag in the microwave on high for 25 to 30 seconds. (*The mixture should bubble a bit and become somewhat transparent.*)
4. Use a hot mitt to remove the baggie and let it cool for a bit.
5. Once it is cool enough to handle, you can shape the plastic into what the students desire. Then, let it sit overnight to completely harden.
6. Have the students complete the Lab Report on SW pg. 97.

Explanation
The students should see that have created a soft moldable plastic that hardens when left overnight. As the cornstarch heats up, it reacts with the water and oil to create a polymer, which is the basic of plastics.

Take it Further
Have the students make a different kind of bioplastic using milk and vinegar. The directions for this can be found at the following website:

🖱 https://sciencebob.com/make-plastic-milk/

Science-Oriented Books

Reading Assignments
📖 *Basher Engineering pg. 68 Concrete, pg. 70 Steel, pg. 76 Plastic*
(Optional) Additional topics to explore this week: *Basher Engineering pg. 72 Glass, pg. 74 Aluminum*

Discussion Questions
After reading the selected pages, ask the following questions for your discussion time.

Concrete
- **?** What is concrete made from?
- **?** How is concrete useful for building?

Steel
- **?** What is steel made from?
- **?** How is steel useful for building?

Plastic
- **?** What is plastic made from?
- **?** Why is plastic a useful material?

(Optional) Additional Books
- 📖 *Concrete Mixers (Blastoff! Readers: Mighty Machines, Level 1)* by Ray McClellan
- 📖 *Steel (Recycle, Reduce, Reuse, Rethink)* by Kate Walker
- 📖 *Plastic (Everyday Materials)* by Andrew Langley
- 📖 *Plastic (Reduce, Reuse, Recycle)* by Alexandra Fix
- 📖 *What Milly Did: The Remarkable Pioneer of Plastics Recycling* by Elise Moser and Scot Ritchie

Notebooking

Writing Assignments
- ☐ **Narration Page –** Have the students dictate, copy, or write three to five sentences on concrete, steel, and plastic materials on SW pg. 96.
- ☐ **(Optional) Lapbook –** Have the students add the cover to the Engineering lapbook by cutting out and coloring the cover on pg. 44. Then, have the students glue the sheet onto the front.

Vocabulary
There is no vocabulary for this week.

Multi-week Projects and Activities

Unit Project
✂ **Building Projects –** There is no recommended building project for this week.

Projects for this Week
✂ **Coloring Pages –** Have the students color the following pages from *Physics for the Grammar Stage Coloring Pages*: Materials pg 50.

✂ **Concrete –** Have the students watch the following video on how concrete is made:
  🖱 https://www.youtube.com/watch?v=QmQuBM0H2PQ

✂ **Steel –** Have the students watch the following video on how steel is made:
  🖱 https://www.youtube.com/watch?v=mRA6RY2o9Lg

✂ **Plastic Hunt –** Have the students go on a hunt around the house to find what items are made of plastic. Then, have them create a collage displaying their results. They can draw, cut out, or take and paste the pictures of the items they find.

Memorization

🗣 This week, continue working on memorizing the *The Engineering Design Process* poem. (SW pg. 127)

Quiz

Weekly Quiz

⚲ "Engineering Unit Week 5 Quiz" on SW pg. Q-37.

Quiz Answers

1. Sand, cement, and water
2. True
3. False (*Plastic is an inexpensive substitute for aluminum or glass.*)
4. Answers will vary

Possible Schedules for Week 5

Two Days a Week Schedule	
Day 1	**Day 2**
❑ Read the page on Plastic	❑ Read the page on Concrete and Steel
❑ Add information about plastic materials to the students' Narration Page	❑ Add information about concrete and steel materials to the students' Narration Page
❑ Do the Scientific Demonstration: Bioplastic	❑ Give Engineering Week 5 quiz
❑ Work on memorizing the *The Engineering Design Process* poem	

Five Days a Week Schedule				
Day 1	**Day 2**	**Day 3**	**Day 4**	**Day 5**
❑ Read the page on Concrete	❑ Read the page on Steel	❑ Read the page on Plastic	❑ Do the Scientific Demonstration: Pumps	❑ Give Engineering Week 5 quiz
❑ Add information about concrete materials to the students' Narration Page	❑ Add information about steel materials to the students' Narration Page	❑ Add information about plastic materials to the students' Narration Page	❑ Choose one or more of the additional books to read from this week	
❑ Watch the Concrete Video	❑ Watch the Steel Video	❑ Complete the Plastic Hunt Project		

All Week Long

❑ Work on memorizing the *The Engineering Design Process* poem

174

Week 6: Bridges and Arches Lesson Plans

Scientific Demonstration: Penny Bridge

Supplies Needed
- ✓ Air dry clay
- ✓ Pack of pipe cleaners
- ✓ Plastic cup
- ✓ Pennies

Purpose
This demonstration is meant to allow the students to practice engineering a bridge.

Instructions and Explanation
1. Place two globs of clay about six inches apart on a table or smooth surface.
2. Then, stick a pipe cleaner in one glob of clay and place the other end in the other glob to create a bridge. Repeat this process four more times to create a bridge with a total of five pipe cleaners.
3. Now, have the students place the plastic cup on the top of the bridge. (*You may need to adjust the positioning of the pipe cleaners so that there is a platform for the cup to rest.*) Have them add pennies until the bridge collapses under the weight or the cup falls off. When this happens, have them record the number of pennies on the lab report sheet on SW pg. 99.
4. Next, add five more pipe cleaners in the same manner to create a bridge with a total of ten pipe cleaners.
5. Have the students test the ten-pipe-cleaner bridge using the cup and pennies. When the bridge fails, have them record the number of pennies on the lab report sheet on SW pg. 99.
6. Have the students complete the Lab Report on SW pg. 97.

Results and Explanation
The students should see that the more pipe cleaners they added, the more pennies the pipe cleaner bridge was able to hold. This is because the additional pipe cleaners add more stiffness and stability to the structure.

Take it Further
Have the students try twisting the 5 pipe cleaners together and repeat the demonstration to see how this compares to the five separate pipe cleaners.

Science-Oriented Books

Reading Assignments
📖 *Basher Engineering pg. 86 Arch, pg. 88 Bridge, pg. 90 Tunnel*
(Optional) Additional topics to explore this week: *Basher Engineering pg. 82 Road, pg. 87 Dome*

Discussion Questions

After reading the selected pages, ask the following questions for your discussion time.

Arch

? How does an arch help to support a structure?

? Why is the curved shape of an arch important?

Bridge

? What is the purpose of a bridge?

? What makes up a bridge?

Tunnel

? What is the purpose of a tunnel?

? How are tunnels built?

(Optional) Additional Books

- *Building America - Gateway Arch* by Craig A. Doherty and Katherine M. Doherty
- *Bridges (True Bookengineering Wonders)* by Katie Marsico
- *Building Bridges (Young Engineers)* by Tammy Enz
- *Tunnels (21st Century Junior Library: Extraordinary Engineering)* by Virginia Loh-Hagan Edd
- *The Channel Tunnel (Great Building Feats)* by Sandra Donovan

Notebooking

Writing Assignments

- ☐ **Narration Page –** Have the students dictate, copy, or write three to five sentences on arches, bridges, and tunnels on SW pg. 98.
- ☐ **(Optional) Lapbook –** Have the students complete the Bridges and Tunnels Fold-book on pp. 49 of *Physics for the Grammar Stage Lapbooking Templates*. Have them cut out the template for the mini-book and cover. Then, have the students color the pictures. Have them add a sentence about arches, bridges, and tunnels under the respective sections. Have the students fold the mini-book on the dotted lines and glue on the cover. Finally, have the students glue the mini-book into the lapbook.

Vocabulary

The following definition is a guide. The students' definition does not need to match word for word.

- ✐ **Infrastructure –** A system of roads, bridges, tunnels, and fundamental services that make it possible for us to live in cities and towns. (SW pg. 109)

Multi-week Projects and Activities

Unit Project

- ✂ **Building Projects –** Have the students build one of the projects from the K'nex: Intro to Simple Machines: Gears Kit. After they are done, take a picture of what they created and add the photo, along with a sentence or two of what they learned, to the Building

Projects Diary in the SW on pp. 86. This week, we recommend trying the Phonograph project.

Projects for this Week

✂ **Coloring Pages –** Have the students color the following pages from *Physics for the Grammar Stage Coloring Pages*: Bridges pg. 51, Tunnels pg. 52.

✂ **Arches –** Have the students learn about some natural arches. You can visit the Arches National Park website to learn more about the famous natural arches:
🖱 https://www.nps.gov/arch/index.htm
Or if you are close enough, visit the park in person.

✂ **Straw Bridge –** Have the students build and test a simple straw bridge. You will need a box of straws, tape, a small plastic bin, a plastic cup, and pennies. Have the students brainstorm for ideas on how to build a bridge across the top of the bin using only straws and tape. Once they have a few ideas, have them choose one to build. After they have build the bridges, test their strength by placing the plastic cup on the top of the bridge. Have them add pennies until the bridge collapses under the weight or the cup falls off.

✂ **Tunnel –** Have the students watch a documentary about how the Chunnel, the world's largest underwater tunnel, was built:
🖱 https://www.youtube.com/watch?v=e5WWwn-x1FI

Memorization

👤 This week, continue working on memorizing the *The Engineering Design Process* poem. (SW pg. 127)

Quiz

Weekly Quiz

🗲 "Engineering Unit Week 6 Quiz" on SW pg. Q-38.

Quiz Answers

1. Bridges
2. Arches
3. Tunnels
4. Answers will vary

Possible Schedules for Week 6

Two Days a Week Schedule	
Day 1	**Day 2**
❑ Read the page on the Bridge ❑ Add information about bridges to the students' Narration Page ❑ Do the Scientific Demonstration: Penny Bridge ❑ Work on memorizing the *The Engineering Design Process* poem	❑ Read the page on the Arch and the Tunnel ❑ Add information about arches and tunnels to the students' Narration Page ❑ Define infrastructure ❑ Work on one of the Building Projects ❑ Give Engineering Week 6 quiz

Five Days a Week Schedule				
Day 1	**Day 2**	**Day 3**	**Day 4**	**Day 5**
❑ Read the page on the Arch ❑ Add information about arches to the students' Narration Page ❑ Complete the Arches Project	❑ Read the page on the Bridge ❑ Add information about bridges to the students' Narration Page ❑ Complete the Straw Bridge Project	❑ Do the Scientific Demonstration: Penny Bridge ❑ Define infrastructure ❑ Choose one or more of the additional books to read from this week	❑ Read the page on the Tunnel ❑ Add information about tunnels to the students' Narration Page ❑ Watch the Tunnel Video	❑ Give Engineering Week 6 quiz ❑ Work on one of the Building Projects
All Week Long				
❑ Work on memorizing the *The Engineering Design Process* poem				

Week 7: Modern Machines Lesson Plans

Scientific Demonstration: Lift Off

Supplies Needed
- ✓ Sheet of paper
- ✓ Scissors
- ✓ String
- ✓ Ruler
- ✓ Tape

Purpose
This demonstration is meant to help the students see how a kite's tail affects flight.

Instructions and Explanation
The instructions and explanation for this scientific demonstration are found on pp. 96-97 of *Janice VanCleave's Physics for Every Kid.* Have the students complete the Lab Report on SW pg. 101.

Take it Further
Have the students do another simple machine-related demonstration - "Paper Flop" on pp. 98-99 of *Janice VanCleave's Physics for Every Kid.*

Science-Oriented Books

Reading Assignments
📖 *Basher Engineering pg. 96 Car, pg. 98 Plane, pg. 100 Submarine*
(Optional) Additional topics to explore this week: *Usborne Science Encyclopedia pp. 140-141 Ships and Boats, pp. 144-145 Aircraft Design, pp. 150-151 Cars and Motorcycles*

Discussion Questions
After reading the selected pages, ask the following questions for your discussion time.

Car
? How does a car work?

Plane
? How does a plane work?

Submarine
? How does a submarine work?

(Optional) Additional Books
- 📖 *Cars, Trains, Ships, and Planes* by DK Publishing
- 📖 *Car Science* by Richard Hammond
- 📖 *I Wonder Why Planes Have Wings: And Other Questions About Transportation* by Christopher Maynard
- 📖 *Submarines (Rookie Read-about Science: How Things Work)* by Joanne Mattern

📖 *DK Readers L1: Submarines and Submersibles* by Deborah Lock

Notebooking

Writing Assignments
- ☐ **Narration Page** – Have the students dictate, copy, or write three to five sentences on modern machines on SW pg. 100.
- ☐ **(Optional) Lapbook** – Have the students complete the Modern Machines Pocket Guide on pp. 50-51 of *Physics for the Grammar Stage Lapbooking Templates.* Have them cut out the pages for the pocket and the cards. Then, have the students color the pictures. Have them add a sentence about how the machine works or how the machine helps us on each card. Finally, have the students glue the pocket into the lapbook and insert the cards.

Vocabulary
The following definition is a guide. The students' definition does not need to match word for word.
- ✏ **Buoyancy** – The way an object sinks or floats in either air or water. (SW pg. 105)

Multi-week Projects and Activities

Unit Project
- ✂ **Building Projects** – Have the students build one of the projects from the K'nex: Intro to Simple Machines: Gears Kit. After they are done, take a picture of what they created and add the photo, along with a sentence or two of what they learned, to the Building Projects Diary in the SW on pp. 86. This week, we recommend trying the Car Window project.

Projects for this Week
- ✂ **Coloring Pages** – Have the students color the following pages from *Physics for the Grammar Stage Coloring Pages*: Buoyancy pg. 53.
- ✂ **Solar Car** – Have the students make a solar powered car from a kit or from Legos. If you make one out of Legos, you will need a few Lego parts to build a car, a Lego gear, Lego axles, a small 9v solar panel, a mini 6 v motor with wires connected to it, and Krazy Glue for this activity. Directions for building a solar-powered Lego car can be found here:
  - 🖱 https://teachbesideme.com/solar-powered-lego-car/
- ✂ **Paper Planes** – Have the students test several paper airplane designs. You will need several sheets of paper for this activity. Have the students make several different paper airplane designs. Then have them launch each one to see which design goes the farthest. If you need ideas for paper airplane designs, check out these 10 options:
  - 🖱 http://www.instructables.com/id/How-to-Make-10-Awesome-Paper-Airplanes/

✂ **Penny Boat –** Have the students test the buoyancy of an aluminum boat. You will need aluminum foil, pennies, and a plastic tub for this activity. Have the students use the aluminum to create a boat or raft to hold pennies. Fill the tub with water and place the boat on the water. Then, have the students add pennies and observe what happens.

Memorization

🗣 This week, continue working on memorizing the *The Engineering Design Process* poem. (SW pg. 127)

Quiz

Weekly Quiz

↯ "Engineering Unit Week 7 Quiz" on SW pg. Q-39.

Quiz Answers

1. Buoyancy is the way an object sinks or floats in either air or water.
2. False (*Submarines do float. They control the amount they sink or float using water.*)
3. True
4. Answers will vary

Possible Schedules for Week 7

Two Days a Week Schedule	
Day 1	**Day 2**
❏ Read the page on the Plane	❏ Read the page on the Car and Submarine
❏ Add information about planes to the students' Narration Page	❏ Add information about cars and submarines to the students' Narration Page
❏ Do the Scientific Demonstration: Lift Off	❏ Define buoyancy
❏ Work on memorizing the *The Engineering Design Process* poem	❏ Work on one of the Building Projects
	❏ Give Engineering Week 7 quiz

Five Days a Week Schedule				
Day 1	**Day 2**	**Day 3**	**Day 4**	**Day 5**
❏ Read the page on the Car	❏ Read the page on the Plane	❏ Do the Scientific Demonstration: Lift Off	❏ Read the page on the Submarine	❏ Give Engineering Week 7 quiz
❏ Add information about cars to the students' Narration Page	❏ Add information about planes to the students' Narration Page	❏ Define buoyancy	❏ Add information about submarines to the students' Narration Page	❏ Work on one of the Building Projects
❏ Complete the Solar Car Project	❏ Complete the Paper Airplanes Project	❏ Choose one or more of the additional books to read from this week	❏ Complete the Penny Boat Project	

All Week Long

❏ Work on memorizing the *The Engineering Design Process* poem

Week 8: Digital Machines Lesson Plans

Scientific Demonstration: Geo-caching

Supplies Needed
- ✓ Smartphone or GPS device
- ✓ Geo-caching app (*available for Apple and Android*)

Purpose
This demonstration is meant to help the students practice using smartphones and GPS to find a cache. (**Note**—*If you do not have access to a smartphone or GPS device, choose one of the optional activities to do instead.*)

Instructions
1. Visit the following website to see how geo-caching works: https://www.geocaching.com/play
2. Download the app and find a cache near you.
3. Use your phone or GPS device to locate the cache! (**Note**—*There is no lab report for this week.*)

Take it Further
Have the students find another geo-cache or hide one of your own!

Science-Oriented Books

Reading Assignments
📖 *Basher Engineering pg. 118 Smartphones, pg. 120 GPS, pg. 122 Robots*
(Optional) Additional topics to explore this week: *Basher Engineering pg. 114 Microchip*

Discussion Questions
After reading the selected pages, ask the following questions for your discussion time.

Smartphones
- **?** What is a smartphone?
- **?** How does a smartphone work?

GPS
- **?** What does GPS stand for?
- **?** How does GPS work?

Robots
- **?** What is a robot?

(Optional) Additional Books
- 📖 *Smartphones (How It Works)* by Lisa J. Amstutz
- 📖 *Satellites and the GPS (Simply Science)* by Natalie M. Rosinsky
- 📖 *National Geographic Readers: Robots* by Melissa Stewart

Notebooking

Writing Assignments

- ☐ **Narration Page –** Have the students dictate, copy, or write three to five sentences on digital machines on SW pg. 102.
- ☐ **(Optional) Lapbook –** Have the students complete the Digital Machines Mini-book on pp. 52 of *Physics for the Grammar Stage Lapbooking Templates*. Have them cut out the digital machines phone mini-book template, color the pictures, and fold the mini-book in half. Have the students write a sentence or two about the digital machines they learned about this week on the inside. Finally, have the students glue the mini-book into the lapbook.

Vocabulary

The following definition is a guide. The students' definition does not need to match word for word.

- ✐ **Robot –** A machine that does routine tasks on command. (SW pg. 115)

Multi-week Projects and Activities

Unit Project

- ✂ **Building Projects –** Have the students build one of the projects from the K'nex: Intro to Simple Machines: Gears Kit. After they are done, take a picture of what they created and add the photo, along with a sentence or two of what they learned, to the Building Projects Diary in the SW on pp. 87. This week, we recommend trying the Crank Fan project.

Projects for this Week

- ✂ **Coloring Pages –** Have the students color the following pages from *Physics for the Grammar Stage Coloring Pages*: Robot pg. 54.
- ✂ **Smartphone Reverse Engineering –** Have the students take apart an old smartphone to see what is inside. You can refer back to week 4 of the Electricity Unit for more directions on this project.
- ✂ **GPS –** Have the students do some research about GPS and write a short report. The report should include what GPS is, what led to the creation of GPS, and several of the key uses of GPS.
- ✂ **Wigglebot –** Have the students build a simple robot. You will need a cup, electrical tape, 3 markers or pens, 2-AAA-battery holder, 2 AAA batteries, 1.5-3 V DC motor with wires, a clothespin, a popsicle stick, googly eyes, and glue for this project. Directions for making a wigglebot can be found at the following website:
  - ☞ https://researchparent.com/homemade-wigglebot/

Memorization

This week, continue working on memorizing the *The Engineering Design Process* poem. (SW pg. 127)

Quiz

Weekly Quiz

- "Engineering Unit Week 8 Quiz" on SW pg. Q-40.

Quiz Answers

1. True
2. GPS stands for Global Positioning System.
3. Robot
4. Answers will vary

Possible Schedules for Week 8

Two Days a Week Schedule	
Day 1	**Day 2**
❑ Read the page on GPS ❑ Add information about GPS to the students' Narration Page ❑ Do the Scientific Demonstration: Geocaching ❑ Work on memorizing the *The Engineering Design Process* poem	❑ Read the page on Smartphones and Robots ❑ Add information about smartphones and robots to the students' Narration Page ❑ Define robot ❑ Work on one of the Building Projects ❑ Give Engineering Week 8 quiz

Five Days a Week Schedule				
Day 1	**Day 2**	**Day 3**	**Day 4**	**Day 5**
❑ Read the page on Smartphones ❑ Add information about smartphones to the students' Narration Page ❑ Complete the Smartphone Reverse Engineering Project	❑ Read the page on GPS ❑ Add information about GPS to the students' Narration Page ❑ Complete the GPS Research Project	❑ Do the Scientific Demonstration: Geocaching ❑ Define robot ❑ Choose one or more of the additional books to read from this week	❑ Read the page on Robots ❑ Add information about robots to the students' Narration Page ❑ Complete the Wigglebot Project	❑ Give Engineering Week 8 quiz ❑ Work on one of the Building Projects
All Week Long				
❑ Work on memorizing the *The Engineering Design Process* poem				

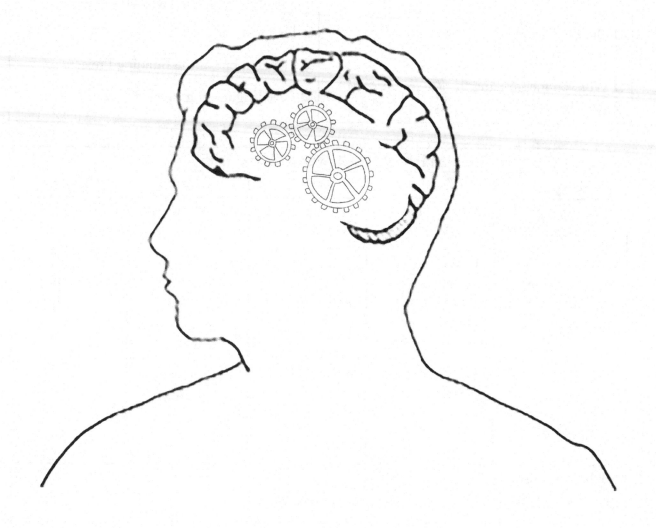

Physics for the Grammar Stage

Appendix

Pinwheel Template

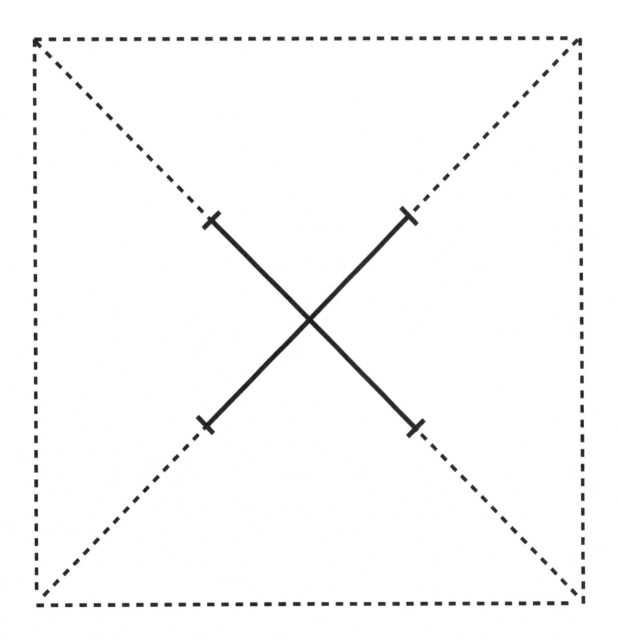

Balance

Balance exists when there is an even distribution of weight that allows someone or something to remain upright or steady.

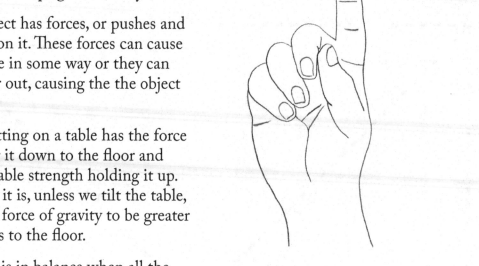

Every object has forces, or pushes and pulls, that act upon it. These forces can cause an object to move in some way or they can cancel each other out, causing the the object to remain at rest.

A book sitting on a table has the force of gravity pulling it down to the floor and the force of the table strength holding it up. It remains where it is, unless we tilt the table, which causes the force of gravity to be greater and the book falls to the floor.

An object is in balance when all the forces that push or pull on it have caused it to remain still.

Christopher Columbus and Balance

There is a popular story about Christopher Columbus and balance. The story says that several of his critics were trying to downplay his discovery of the Americas and to question Columbus's intelligence.

So, Christopher challenged them to make an egg stand on its tip. After much effort, they gave up. Columbus stepped up and tapped the egg on the table, flattening the eggshell on the tip, and the egg was able to stand upright with little effort.

Now, he did crack the egg in the process, but the story says that he silenced his critics by proving that he was the smarter man.

The Engineering Design Process

An engineer creates things that we use, such as cars, toys, computers, and more! Engineers use science, math, and their own curiosity to design products and processes that meet needs and solve problems. The way the engineers do this is through an eight-step process known as the engineering design process.

The process begins with identifying the design goal for a new product or process. The engineer will ask if the design is trying to solve a problem, to improve an existing product or process, or meet a need. Once the engineer has this information, he or she will ask questions to clarify the goal of the design. To do this, the engineer will do a bit of research – he or she may interview users, collect information about the topic, or investigate how the problem has been addressed in the past.

Once the engineer has completed the research, he or she will revisit the design goal and rewrite it, based on the research information. The purpose here is to make sure that the design goal can be achieved and that the design will truly meet the need or solve the original problem. Now that the engineer has a clearly defined goal, it's time to brainstorm for ideas! The engineer will come up with lots of ideas, some practical and some crazy, and will write all those ideas down.

After the engineer has brainstormed, he or she will look over the list and evaluate which idea will be most likely to meet the design goal. Often, engineers will collaborate and discuss their ideas so that they select the most appropriate idea for the next step, which is to design and build a prototype. A prototype is a working model that allows an engineer to test the idea selected.

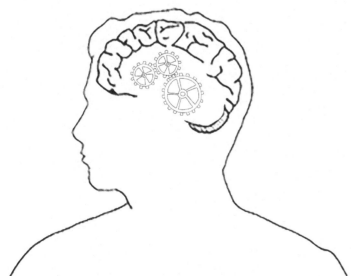

In the seventh step, the engineer takes the prototype and tests it to see if it will meet the design goal. Frequently, the prototype will not pass the test, so for the final step, the engineer will go back and redesign the prototype. The engineer will then make the necessary changes and test the prototype again.

By following these eight steps, engineers can design products and processes that meet our needs and solve our problems.

Physics for the Grammar Stage

Glossary

A

- **Acceleration** – A change in the speed or direction of an object.

B

- **Balance** – The point at which all the forces acting on an object cancel each other out.
- **Battery** – A source of stored electrical energy.
- **Binary Code** – A way of representing information using only 1's and 0's.
- **Buoyancy** – The way an object sinks or floats in either air or water.

C

- **Capacitor** – A device that stores electrical energy until it is needed.
- **Centripetal force** – A force that keeps an object moving in a circle.
- **Circuit** – The path along which electrical current flows.
- **Conduction** – The transfer of heat through direct contact.
- **Conductor** – A substance through which current can flow.
- **Convection** – The transfer of heat through the movement of a liquid and gas.

D

- **Decibel (dB)** – The unit of loudness.
- **Density** – A measure of the amount of matter (mass) in a substance compared to its volume.

E

- **Electricity** – The effect caused by the presence or movement of electrically charged particles.
- **Energy** – The ability to do work.
- **Energy Chain** – A way of showing how energy changes into different forms.
- **Engine** – A machine that converts stored energy into movement.
- **Engineer** – A person who uses science and math to design products and processes that meet needs and solve problems.

F

- **Force** – A push or pull on an object.

- **Friction** – The force that causes moving objects to slow down when they are touching.

G

- **Gravity** – The pulling force that attracts objects to each other.

H

- **Heat** – A form of energy that flows from one place to another because of differences in temperature.

I

- **Inertia** – The tendency of objects to resist a change in their movement.

- **Infrastructure** – A system of roads, bridges, tunnels, and fundamental services that make it possible for us to live in cities and towns.

- **Insulator** – A substance through which current cannot flow.

- **Interference** – The effect that occurs when two waves meet.

J

K

L

- **Lens** – A curved transparent surface that causes light to bend in a particular way.

- **Light** – The electromagnetic waves of energy that make objects visible.

- **Load** – The force of an object's weight that a machine needs to overcome.

- **Longitudinal Wave** – A wave that vibrates in the same direction as it travels.

- **Lubricant** – A substance used to reduce friction.

M

- **Magnet** – An object that attracts iron, steel, and metals.

- **Mass** – The amount of matter contained in an object.

- **Mirror** – A shiny surface that reflects nearly all the light that hits it.

- **Momentum** – A measure of an object's tendency to continue moving.

N

- **Nuclear fission** – The splitting apart of atomic particles to create energy.

- **Nuclear fusion** – The joining of atomic particles to create energy.

O

P

- **Pole** – One of the two points on a magnet where the force of attraction or repulsion is strongest.

- **Primary colors** – Colors from which all other colors can be made. The primary colors are red, yellow, and blue.

- **Prototype** – A working model that allows engineers to test their idea.

Q

R

- **Radiation** – The transfer of heat through indirect contact.

- **Reflection** – The change in direction of light rays that occurs when it hits an object and bounces off.

- **Refraction** – The bending of light rays caused by light passing through substances with different densities.

- **Resistor** – An electrical component that reduces the flow of current.

- **Resonate** – To vibrate at the same frequency as something else.

- **Resultant force** – The combined effect of the forces acting on an object.

- **Robot** – A machine that does routine tasks on command.

S

- **Secondary colors** – Colors that can be made by mixing two primary colors. The secondary colors are orange, green, and purple.
- **Shadow** – A dark area that is formed when an object blocks out light waves.
- **Simple Machine** – A device, such as a lever or a pulley, that helps to multiply the effort in order to move a load.
- **Solar energy** – Energy from the sun.
- **Sound Wave** – A mechanical wave that carries sound energy through a medium.
- **Speed** – A measure of how fast an object is moving.

T

- **Temperature** – A measure of how much heat an object has.
- **Torque** – The force you add to make something rotate.
- **Transverse Wave** – A wave that vibrates at right angles to the direction of travel.

U

V

W

- **Weight** – A measure of the strength of the pull of gravity on an object.
- **Wind energy** – Energy from the wind.
- **Work** – Something that is done when a force moves an object.

X

Y

Z

Physics for the Grammar Stage

General Templates

Project Record Sheet

Paste a picture of your
project in this box.

What I Learned:

_____

_____

_____

_____

_____

_____

_____

Two Days a Week Schedule

Day 1	Day 2
❑	❑
❑	❑
❑	❑
❑	❑
❑	❑
❑	❑

Things to Prepare

❑

❑

❑

Notes

Five Days a Week Schedule

Day 1	Day 2	Day 3	Day 4	Day 5
❑	❑	❑	❑	❑
❑	❑	❑	❑	❑
❑	❑	❑	❑	❑
❑	❑	❑	❑	❑

All Week Long

❑

❑

Things to Prepare

❑

❑

❑

Notes